ECHOES
OF
WAR

A PUBLICATION OF

Literature & Medicine

humanities at the heart of health care

A PROGRAM OF THE
MAINE HUMANITIES COUNCIL

PUBLISHED WITH FUNDING FROM

NATIONAL ENDOWMENT FOR THE HUMANITIES
MAINE HUMANITIES COUNCIL

ECHOES
OF
WAR

EDITED BY
SUZANNE HUNTER BROWN

A LITERATURE AND MEDICINE ANTHOLOGY

14 13 12 11 10 09   6 5 4 3 2 1

Publisher Cataloging-in-Publication Data
Echoes of war : a literature and medicine anthology /
edited by Suzanne Hunter Brown.
     p. cm.
   Includes bibliographic references.
   ISBN 978-0-615-28180-3 (pbk : acid-free paper)
   1. Medicine—Literary collections.   I. Brown, Suzanne Hunter, 1954 –

Designed by Lori Harley
Printed by Walch Printing

Echoes of War is dedicated to our country's veterans and their families, and to all the health care professionals who care for them.

We also dedicate this anthology to the memory of Marli Weiner, a crucial partner in the growth and development of *Literature & Medicine* nationally and in Maine.

CONTENTS

ACKNOWLEDGMENTS

This anthology grows out of a new initiative of *Literature & Medicine: Humanities at the Heart of Health Care,*® a reading and discussion program for health care professionals that "renews the heart and soul of health care." *Literature & Medicine* is already in over twenty states nationwide, and now, in its second decade, will also be offered to health care professionals in Veterans Administration health care facilities thanks to major support from the National Endowment for the Humanities.

The opportunity to reflect on their professional roles and relationships through the lens of literature, and to have the opportunity to share insights with colleagues, has proved to have a significant effect on the way health care professionals understand their work and their relationships with patients and each other. It improves their communication and interpersonal skills, and increases their cultural awareness, empathy for patients and job satisfaction. We hope that the poems, short stories and essays in *Echoes of War* will help the health care professionals who work with veterans to better understand the experiences of soldiers who have been to war, the difficulties of homecoming for both the soldiers and their families, and the kinds of issues that are likely to emerge in the process of caring for those who have served. Some of the selections may, as well, offer health care professionals insight into their own responses. We also believe that the anthology will be of interest and value to any reader who seeks greater understanding of the issues faced by our veterans, and who is interested in new perspectives on their own and others' experiences. Finally, we hope that *Echoes of War* will make a contribution, in a small way, to the veterans who have served, and may still suffer for, their country.

I want to thank our editor, Suzanne Hunter Brown, who has been amazingly agile, fast thinking and flexible in meeting the unreasonable if not absolutely impossible deadlines we had to set to pull *Echoes of War* together. The same must be said of the anthology's designer, Lori Harley, who, under the limitations of a strict budget as well as a short time line, once again delivered a product we are proud of. I have also relied upon members of the Maine Humanities Council staff, particularly Martina Duncan, Erik Jorgensen, Annie Medeiros, Karen Myrick, Jessica Pyle-Carter and Lizz Sinclair, and am grateful for their help. Amy Levin, Laurie Quinn and Gregory Waters, dedicated *Literature & Medicine* scholars, have made numerous helpful suggestions for the contents of *Echoes of War*. And of course, without funding from the National Endowment for the Humanities, this volume and the program that it supports would not exist.

Victoria Bonebakker, May 2009
Literature & Medicine Project Director

INTRODUCTION

Echoes of War is intended for health care professionals in Veterans Administration facilities, and therefore the selections focus on issues unique to, or more acute in, hospitals for soldiers. Nevertheless, any group of health care professionals could profit from the readings, both because all health care facilities will increasingly see veterans, and because "veterans' issues" often illuminate general medical concerns. We hope too that the general public will appreciate these readings as a way to better understand the experience of the men and women who fight for us, if only as one way to narrow the "chasm" Matthew Bogdanos warned of in *The Washington Post*, "with the military and civilian worlds warily eyeing each other across a cultural no man's land." He points out that in the 1970s, 74 percent of Congress had prior military service in contrast to 23 percent today, and that President Obama has only two veterans in his Cabinet—"the fewest since Herbert Hoover." Bumper stickers urge us to "Support Our Troops," and the scandal surrounding the treatment of soldiers in Walter Reed Hospital—a Department of Defense, not a VA facility—showed that civilians do care about soldiers' welfare. Bogdanos suggests, however, that such good will is not enough: "The solution is an educated citizenry that understands its soldiers, sailors, and airmen and Marines—understands that we are you." The portfolio of photographs by Platon included in this volume offers a visual introduction to these Americans—training for, traveling to, engaging in and then returning from war.

Even in the face of very public support for veterans, those away at war often feel that they cannot communicate their experience to anyone at home, and the resulting chasm creates pressure for returnees and their families. This worry can compound a more general medical problem: the severely ill often doubt that the healthy can fully comprehend their reality. In "Desert Places," Robert Frost evokes just such a terrible internal and external landscape as the ultimate despair: "With no expression, nothing to express." While medicine overall is coming to see that treatment should take account of a patient's home situation, VA hospital staff members have long known that understanding the potential disconnection between patients and their families is crucial. Thus homecoming complicates the medical issues warriors face. Over a century before we saw soldiers repeating tours in Viet Nam and Iraq, Tennyson, in "Ulysses" and "The Lotos-Eaters," understood homecoming as something fighters avoid even as they long for it. Like contemporary psychiatrist Jonathan Shay, Tennyson interprets Homer's *Odyssey* as a tale of reluctant return. Tennyson's veterans in fact prefer the lotos and the dreams it brings, reminding us that substance abuse can be an alternative to the hard work of returning home after war; three times their chorus repeats, "let us alone." Though not a soldier, the alcoholic who narrates "Where I'm Calling From" eventually sees and fears his own isolation; the end of Raymond Carver's story finds him fingering the change he may use to call his girlfriend from the rehab center: "'Hello, sugar,' I'll say when she answers, 'It's me.'"

Homecoming stories are not, however, unrelentingly grim. Frank O'Connor's "My Oedipus Complex" relates a soldier's return from the point of view of the young son who has grown up in his father's absence, and resents his father's reappearance because it disrupts his close relationship with his mother. This story is poignantly funny, and reminds us that young children may see returning parents as strangers. Questions of fidelity and abandonment can also shadow homecoming for spouses. "To Lucasta, on Going to the Wars" contains the famous seventeenth-century justification of a soldier's leaving his love behind: "I could not love you, dear, so much/ Loved I not honor more." In "War Song" the woman left behind speaks; she understands and seems to accept that separation strains sexual fidelity. George Garrett's "Wounded Soldier (Cartoon Strip)" emphasizes the larger cultural tensions surrounding homecoming when the severely disfigured Veteran is asked to remain in the hospital because "his appearance in public, in the city or the country, would probably serve to arouse the anguish of the civilian population."

Families also need support because the anger veterans may feel is often visited on those closest to them. Anne Brashler's short story "He Read to Her" reminds us that all patients can lash out when their bodies betray them. The fury of the middle-aged woman after her colostomy may seem remote from the anger of those returning from a war zone, but many health care providers will sympathize—both with her and with the husband on the receiving end of that fury when she yells, "I don't want tea! Just leave me alone." Sometimes the best discussions about important issues occur when those central concerns are slightly displaced in literature, mirrored yet also distanced. The husband in Brashler's story seems to understand this when he chooses *Moby Dick*, the tale of Ahab's furious pursuit of the white whale that has taken his leg, to read to his angry wife. We have therefore included in this reader pieces that address veterans' issues obliquely as well as directly. Using both approaches simultaneously respects the uniqueness of those issues and connects them to other aspects of medical—and human—experience. The very title of "The Use of Force" compares the doctor in the story to a soldier. This work by William Carlos Williams probes the visceral anger aroused when anyone employs force even in "a good cause." "Out of the Snow" by Andre Dubus makes it clear that women can "enjoy" violence too; however, gender expectations may make it even harder for our female soldiers to come to terms with such feelings.

Patients whose multiple physical ailments are entwined with their social circumstances are difficult to treat and may frustrate caregivers. The nurse in "Bev Brown" at first avoids talking to the suicidal "frequent flyer" whose problems are overwhelming: poverty, Parkinson's disease, stress incontinence, childhood trauma and sexual abuse, obesity. When she does enter the room, because "after all, this *was* my job," she feels she can only offer "a fountain of platitudes, which I hovered on the verge of believing," not sure herself that Bev has a reason to live: "And though one voice inside me said: *your words are crumbs, crusts, parings,* another voice said: *people can live on them. And do.*" This nurse amuses the rest of the staff by dubbing Bev "Jabba the Hut," but she also reads Bev's poems. Near the end of the story she explains how black humor can coexist with caring: "When we make fun of the patients, it's like we're ducks on the shore, preening our feathers. We'd sink if we didn't." The doctor in "The Girl with a Pimply Face" treats a baby whose impoverished family also faces seemingly insurmountable problems. In this case he finds it hard to help the child because he isn't sure that he can believe what the mother tells him; how much are her stories of suffering and destitution an attempt to exploit and manipulate his sympathies?—a question that also haunts the doctor in "An Infected Heart." The speaker in Veneta Masson's poem finds it similarly difficult to untangle the listener's physical ailments from the problems of poverty, and may be frustrated that the diabetic woman does not lose weight.

The term "veterans' issue" implies an experience common to all military, but the diversity of the individuals in the armed forces assures that these issues will play out differently in different cases. Over a third of recruits belong to a racial or ethnic minority. The narrator of Louise Erdrich's "The Red Convertible" articulates the sorrow any family member might feel at failing to reach a veteran suffering from depression and PTSD, but Erdrich also suggests that the problems of Stephan, a Chippewa Indian, have an added cultural dimension. With no access to Indian doctors or medicine people, Stephan's mother rejects for her son treatment in the white man's hospital, fearing the doctors will simply keep him there. The significance of Stephan's description of himself as an Indian is more ambiguous, but given its placement in the narrative could be seen as a factor in his sense of hopelessness. The African American speaker in Marilyn Nelson's poem, "Porter," returns home from distinguished war service, only to be tipped by "a little grayhaired white lady" for carrying her suitcase. This and Nelson's other poems draw on her father's service in the Tuskegee Airmen, the WWII corps of pioneering African American pilots. Together these poems present a sometimes contradictory picture of this moment when the Air Force pushed social change: "Freeman Field" records a racist incident, while "Star-Fix" suggests the ways mutual dependency during combat can overcome racism. "Three Men in a Tent" both celebrates integration and mourns the lost closeness of black men housed together. Wanda Coleman's story "Slave Driver" examines racism in a health care setting, making us ponder the best response when we see a co-worker subjected to a patient's mistreatment. Although more women are fighting in Iraq than in any other conflict since WWII, the full integration of women into the armed forces can also generate tensions. Gender stereotypes in both the military and the surrounding culture may complicate recovery from sexual abuse for both men and women. While Mavis Gallant sets "My Heart Is Broken" in a road-construction camp rather than in the army, her story demonstrates the ways victims of sexual abuse may internalize the values of an isolated, predominantly male community when justice for one individual is less of a priority than the smooth functioning of the group. Even the other woman in the camp tells the victim, "Don't say who it was…. We don't any of us need to know." Helen Benedict's recent article cited at the end of this reader claims that current women soldiers are often viewed as traitors for reporting sexual assault.

Because VA hospitals continue to care for soldiers throughout their lives, they confront all the problems of aging even as they receive the young injured veterans of Iraq and Afghanistan. The work of surgeon Atul Gawande covers both ends of the spectrum. His "The Way We Age Now" reports sometimes surprising facts about geriatric medicine, while his "Casualties of War" educates us about the current state of military medicine. We learn that blindness and traumatic brain injury are signature casualties in Iraq, and Gawande outlines the ways our entire health care system can profit from innovations in military medicine. Paradoxically, our ability to save lives that would have been lost in earlier wars brings the greater challenge to rehabilitate more severely disabled veterans. As Gawande puts it, "We have never faced having to rehabilitate people with such extensive wounds. We are only beginning to learn what to do to make a life worth living possible for them." Thus both aging soldiers and young returnees who must reinvent themselves after being wounded face the difficulties of living with a chronic condition. Those who care for either group of veterans will appreciate the humor and painful honesty of "On Being a Cripple." Like Nancy Mairs, Andre Dubus writes about the pain and exhaustion disabled men and women may face, but his "Dancing After Hours" celebrates the intimacy that can accompany our need to depend on each other, and he treats our fear of helplessness as a human struggle affecting all the characters in the story.

Most of this essay has outlined some of the major issues facing those who care for veterans, and has suggested ways specific pieces might bear on those issues. Nevertheless we have not generally classified particular works under these headings. Indeed, we often chose these essays, poems, and stories for the very reason that they touch on so many vital concerns simultaneously. How, for example, to "classify" Arthur Kleinman's essay "Winthrop Cohen"? This case study of a Marine's depression following his service in World War II poses questions of aging (why does his guilt surface only four decades after the original trauma?). Since Winthrop Cohen has risen from the working class to great wealth, class may influence his story. Kleinman postulates that racism may affect Cohen's guilt as he seeks to come to terms with killing. Cohen remembers shooting a "Christlike" Japanese medic and bayoneting a "Jap" he has already shot because "I was uncontrollable, in a rage." As a Jew, he may be haunted by the stereotype of "Christ-killer." Clearly this essay might also be grouped with the Williams story discussed above as a study of the anger unleashed when someone uses force even in a "good" cause. The piece also raises troubling questions for mental health professionals, who, like Kleinman, must consider Cohen's accusation "that I was part of the societal collusion to cover up the threatening implications of war experiences such as his." Nor do these topics exhaust the range of issues the essay raises. They are offered only as possibilities, as examples of the rich connections that can arise when the pieces in this anthology are combined in ways that readers themselves will discover and create.

We hope the very variety of offerings will spur such unexpected and fruitful combinings. Selections deal with Viet Nam ("The Red Convertible"), World War II ("Winthrop Cohen," "Freeman Field"), the current war in Iraq ("AB Negative," "Casualties of War"), the Civil War ("Old War-Dreams"), World War I ("My Oedipus Complex") and the mythical Trojan War ("Ulysses," "The Lotos-Eaters"). This range allows readers to consider both the universal in war, and the way each war generates its own unique circumstances and vocabulary. We have included works by novelists, poets, psychiatrists, soldiers, surgeons, and nurses so that many disciplines can contribute to our understanding; we have chosen short stories, essays, photographs, and poems to reflect the echoes of war in more than one genre.

Despite such variety, *Echoes of War* is not, and is not intended to be, exhaustive. Hospitals for veterans are, first of all, hospitals. Staff there share the same concerns as other health care providers, and most VA reading and discussion groups would want to intersperse these readings with selections from other, more general literature and medicine anthologies. Some groups may want to include longer works, and we provide an annotated list of suggestions in the back of this anthology. *Imagine What It's Like,* a general literature and medicine anthology previously published by the Maine Humanities Council, contains selections, such as Walt Whitman's "The Wound-Dresser," Raymond Carver's "Cathedral," and Pat Staten's "The Day My Father Tried to Kill Us," that bear directly on veterans' issues. In addition, a list of favorite literature readings, an annotated bibliography and information about other resources appear on the Maine Humanities Council web site, www.mainehumanities.org/programs/litandmed/index.html.

Finally, this anthology and the programs it supports rest on our belief in the power of story to foster empathy and imagination. However, success in bridging the gap between the sick and the well, between veterans and those who haven't "been there," may also depend on acknowledging limits; literature may be our best means to get outside our own skins, but it simultaneously makes us understand and respect the power of experiences we cannot fully know.

Suzanne Brown
Dartmouth College

HE READ TO HER

ANNE BRASHLER

She locked the bathroom door, sprayed the small closed room with lemon odor, then removed her robe. The colostomy bag was full and leaking; brown stains seeped down her belly and across old scars, new scars, old stretch marks. Her stomach looked like a map of dirt roads. "Crap," she said. She cupped her hand under the bag, holding it like a third breast, then held her breath long enough to break the seal, remove the bag, and quickly tie its contents into a white plastic container. Her colostomy resembled a brown puckered rose.

The bathroom filled with billowy steam as she stayed under the shower. When her husband rapped on the door, she said, "I'm fine. Leave me alone." As she stepped from the tub, refreshed and clean, the puckered rose exploded with bile, shooting brown stinking liquid over the sink, the mirror, the toilet bowl. Doubling up her right hand, she smashed the mirror to smithereens. Her husband removed the bathroom door and, gagging from the odor, placed her on the sofa bed on the porch, cleaned her off, then dressed her open wound, positioning a clean bag over the plastic rim that held it in place. "There," he said. "Everything's going to be all right. You're going to be just fine."

"I was brushing my hair," she said. "My hand slipped." He pulled mirror slivers out of her fist with tweezers, swabbed the cuts in her hand with witch hazel, saying, "There. That's better."

"Nothing you say or do will make me feel better," she said. She smelled the bile; tasted it at the back of her mouth. She ran her tongue along her teeth, convinced they had turned green. "I want my red bed jacket," she said. "Not this raggedy thing. Why didn't you bring me the red one?"

"I'm fixing tea," he said, running from the room. She heard him gag in the kitchen.

"I don't want tea!" she shouted. "Just leave me alone." The kettle whistled, playing an organ strain from Bach, sounding nervous. She knew he'd bring the tea, the double-crostics book, the reference books. She'd look up the Down answers of the puzzle he'd been working on so that when he got stuck, she'd be able to provide the correct solution, shorten the game. He'd made a cherry wood bed tray, carved flowers around its edges, and was carrying it in, its legs splayed like a little dog flying. "Tea," he said. "Lemon slices, sugar; a rose for my beautiful wife."

"You creep," she said. "That's not going to do any good." She watched his face pale, contort, then smooth out like a person beatified. "I have something different today," he said. He held a book behind him like a surprise.

"Oh yeah?" she said. "It's a quote by Thomas Wolfe from *Look Homeward, Angel.* The definition for Number One Down is 'geometric progression.'" She wished she could hurt him but didn't know how; double-crostics was the best she could do.

"You looked," he said. "But that isn't it. I did that puzzle after you went to bed last night." He puffed pillows into shape, then tucked them under her head, ignoring her when she made her body stiffen. The bag gurgled as liquid hit the plastic.

"Why don't you just leave me alone?" she said and was instantly sorry. Lord knows it wasn't his fault. Lord knows. A joke. Lord, Lord, have mercy. Outside a squirrel chased a blue jay up a willow tree; blue and gray among silvery leaves. Their porch was over the garage, so in summer, with trees filled out, it felt as though they were in the branches of a forest. Their daughter had insisted she recuperate here, in this room, her favorite.

He sat down, ignoring her, then opened the book and began to read in a soft, clear voice: *"Call me Ishmael. Some years ago—never mind how long precisely—having little or no money in my purse, and nothing in particular to interest me on shore, I thought I would sail about a little and see the watery part of the world...."* His face was intense, as if he'd turned into a priest since she'd been away.

"Are you going to read the whole damn book out loud?" she asked. She wondered if she'd be angry for the rest of her life. She'd hoped she'd be able to laugh again, say something nice once in a while.

"I thought I might," he said.

A breeze picked up leaves, turned them over, making different shades of green. The children had guests; they were racing with inner tubes in the pool. Her son had found huge truck tires at a flea market, hosed them off, patched the inner tubes with colored swatches. Her daughter had taken over the household chores while she'd been in the hospital. They'd kept the family running, ship-shape. Her husband, too; he'd had a shock, nearly losing her, going out of his mind with guilt, with self-loathing, the worst kind of pain. "I'd like that, Darly," she finally said. The tea was cold but she drank it anyway.

"Say that again."

"Say what?"

"What you just said."

"Darly? I stole it from some story," she said. Her bag filled suddenly and she thought how convenient it all was.

"I like that. Call me that. Will you call me that?" he asked. He leaned forward, his gray head nestling in the hollow of her shoulder.

"But it's not mine," she said.

"I don't care. I like it."

"Some man said it to his wife. He called her that before they divorced." Was she threatening? Lord knows.

"I don't care," he said.

"Darly," she said, sighing. "Read to me." They'll sort it out later. When cheers for the winner of the inner tube race rose from the pool, she pretended the cheers were for her; she pretended she was a star.

"...*Whenever I find myself growing grim about the mouth; whenever it is a damp, drizzly November in my soul....*" She lay back and closed her eyes. His voice was music; he became Ishmael, telling her a story.

WHERE I'M CALLING FROM

RAYMOND CARVER

J.P. and I are on the front porch at Frank Martin's drying-out facility. Like the rest of us at Frank Martin's, J.P. is first and foremost a drunk. But he's also a chimney sweep. It's his first time here, and he's scared. I've been here once before. What's to say? I'm back. J.P.'s real name is Joe Penny, but he says I should call him J.P. He's about thirty years old. Younger than I am. Not much younger, but a little. He's telling me how he decided to go into his line of work, and he wants to use his hands when he talks. But his hands tremble. I mean, they won't keep still. "This has never happened to me before," he says. He means the trembling. I tell him I sympathize. I tell him the shakes will idle down. And they will. But it takes time.

We've only been in here a couple of days. We're not out of the woods yet. J.P. has these shakes, and every so often a nerve—maybe it isn't a nerve, but it's something—begins to jerk in my shoulder. Sometimes it's at the side of my neck. When this happens, my mouth dries up. It's an effort just to swallow then. I know something's about to happen and I want to head it off. I want to hide from it, that's what I want to do. Just close my eyes and let it pass by, let it take the next man. J.P. can wait a minute.

I saw a seizure yesterday morning. A guy they call Tiny. A bit fat guy, an electrician from Santa Rosa. They said he'd been in here for nearly two weeks and that he was over the hump. He was going home in a day or two and would spend New Year's Eve with his wife in front of the TV. On New Year's Eve, Tiny planned to drink hot chocolate and eat cookies. Yesterday morning he seemed just fine when he came down for breakfast. He was letting out with quacking noises, showing some guy how he called ducks right down onto his head. "Blam. Blam," said Tiny, picking off a couple. Tiny's hair was damp and was slicked back along the sides of his head. He'd just come out of the shower. He'd also nicked himself on the chin with his razor. But so what? Just about everybody at Frank Martin's has nicks on his face. It's something that happens. Tiny edged in at the head of the table and began telling about something that had happened on one of his drinking bouts. People at the table laughed and shook their heads as they shoveled up their eggs. Tiny would say something, grin, then look around the table for a sign of recognition. We'd all done things just as bad and crazy, so, sure, that's why we laughed. Tiny had scrambled eggs on his plate, and some biscuits and honey. I was at the table, but I wasn't hungry. I had some coffee in front of me. Suddenly, Tiny wasn't there anymore. He'd gone over in his chair with a big clatter. He was on his back on the floor with his eyes closed, his heels drumming the linoleum. People hollered for Frank Martin. But he was right there. A couple of guys got down on the floor beside Tiny. One of the guys put his fingers inside Tiny's mouth and tried to hold his tongue. Frank Martin yelled, "Everybody stand back!" Then I noticed that the bunch of us were leaning over Tiny, just looking at him, not able to take our eyes off him. "Give him air!" Frank Martin said. Then he ran into the office and called the ambulance.

Tiny is on board again today. Talk about bouncing back. This morning Frank Martin drove the station wagon to the hospital to get him. Tiny got back too late for his eggs, but he took some coffee into the dining room and sat down at the table anyway. Somebody in the kitchen made toast for him, but Tiny didn't eat it. He just sat with his coffee and looked into his cup. Every now and then he moved his cup back and forth in front of him.

I'd like to ask him if he had any signal just before it happened. I'd like to know if he felt his ticker skip a beat, or else begin to race. Did his eyelid twitch? But I'm not about to say anything. He doesn't look like he's hot to talk about it, anyway. But what happened to Tiny is something I won't ever forget. Old Tiny flat on the floor, kicking his heels. So every time this little flitter starts up anywhere, I draw some breath and wait to find myself on my back, looking up, somebody's fingers in my mouth.

* * * * *

In his chair on the front porch, J.P. keeps his hands in his lap. I smoke cigarettes and use an old coal bucket for an ashtray. I listen to J.P. ramble on. It's eleven o'clock in the morning—an hour and a half until lunch. Neither one of us is hungry. But just the same we look forward to going inside and sitting down at the table. Maybe we'll get hungry.

What's J.P. talking about, anyway? He's saying how when he was twelve years old he fell into a well in the vicinity of the farm he grew up on. It was a dry well, lucky for him. "Or unlucky," he says, looking around him and shaking his head. He says how late that afternoon, after he'd been located, his dad hauled him out with a rope. J.P. had wet his pants down there. He'd suffered all kinds of terror in that well, hollering for help, waiting, and then hollering some more. He hollered himself hoarse before it was over. But he told me that being at the bottom of that well had made a lasting impression. He'd sat there and looked up at the well mouth. Way up at the top, he could see a circle of blue sky. Every once in a while a white cloud passed over. A flock of birds flew across, and it seemed to J.P. their wingbeats set up this odd commotion. He heard other things. He heard tiny rustlings above him in the well, which made him wonder if things might fall down into his hair. He was thinking of insects. He heard wind blow over the well mouth, and that sound made an impression on him, too. In short, everything about his life was different for him at the bottom of that well. But nothing fell on him and nothing closed off that little circle of blue. Then his dad come along with the rope, and it wasn't long before J.P. was back in the world he'd always lived in.

"Keep talking, J.P. Then what?" I say.

When he was eighteen or nineteen years old and out of high school and had nothing whatsoever he wanted to do with his life, he went across town one afternoon to visit a friend. This friend lived in a house with a fireplace. J.P. and his friend sat around drinking beer and batting the breeze. They played some records. Then the doorbell rings. The friend goes to the door. This young woman chimney sweep is there with her cleaning things. She's wearing a top hat, the sight of which knocked J.P. for a loop. She tells J.P.'s friend that she has an appointment to clean the fireplace. The friend lets her in and bows. The young woman doesn't pay him any mind. She spreads a blanket on the hearth and lays out her gear. She's wearing these black pants, black shirt, black shoes and socks. Of course, by now she's taken her hat off. J.P. says it nearly drove him nuts to look at her. She does the work, she cleans the chimney, while J.P. and his friend play records and drink beer. But they watch her and they watch what she does. Now and then J.P. and his friend look at each other and grin, or else they wink. They raise their eyebrows when the upper half of the young woman disappears into the chimney. She was all-right looking, too, J.P. said.

When she'd finished her work, she rolled her things up in the blanket. From J.P.'s friend, she took a check that had been made out to her by his parents. And then she asks the friend if he wants to kiss her. "It's supposed to bring good luck," she says. That does it for J.P. The friend rolls his eyes. He clowns some more. Then, probably blushing, he kisses her on the cheek. At this minute, J.P. made his mind up about something. He put his beer down. He got up from the sofa. He went over to the young woman as she was starting to go out the door.

"Me, too?" J.P. said to her.

She swept her eyes over him. J.P. says he could feel his heart knocking. The young woman's name, it turns out, was Roxy.

"Sure," Roxy says. "Why not? I've got some extra kisses." And she kissed him a good one right on the lips and then turned to go.

Like that, quick as a wink, J.P. followed her onto the porch. He held the porch screen door for her. He went down the steps with her and out to the drive, where she'd parked her panel truck. It was something that was out of his hands. Nothing else in the world counted for anything. He knew he'd met somebody who could set his legs atremble. He could feel her kiss still burning on his lips, etc. J.P. couldn't begin to sort anything out. He was filled with sensations that were carrying him every which way.

He opened the rear door of the panel truck for her. He helped her store her things inside. "Thanks," she told him. Then he blurted it out—that he'd like to see her again. Would she go to a movie with him sometime? He'd realized, too, what he wanted to do with his life. He wanted to do what she did. He wanted to be a chimney sweep. But he didn't tell her that then.

J.P. says she put her hands on her hips and looked him over. Then she found a business card in the front seat of her truck. She gave it to him. She said, "Call this number after ten tonight. We can talk. I have to go now." She put the top hat on and then took it off. She looked at J.P. once more. She must have liked what she saw, because this time she grinned. He told her there was a smudge near her mouth. Then she got into her truck, tooted the horn, and drove away.

"Then what?" I say. "Don't stop now, J.P."

I was interested. But I would have listened if he'd been going on about how one day he'd decided to start pitching horseshoes.

* * * * *

It rained last night. The clouds are banked up against the hills across the valley. J.P. clears his throat and looks at the hills and the clouds. He pulls his chin. Then he goes on with what he was saying.

Roxy starts going out with him on dates. And little by little he talks her into letting him go along on jobs with her. But Roxy's in business with her father and brother and they've got just the right amount of work. They don't need anybody else. Besides, who was this guy J.P.? J.P. what? Watch out, they warned her.

So she and J.P. saw some movies together. They went to a few dances. But mainly the courtship revolved around their cleaning chimneys together. Before you know it, J.P. says, they're talking about tying the knot. And after a while they do it, they get married. J.P.'s new father-in-law takes him in as a full partner. In a year or so, Roxy has a kid. She's quit being a chimney sweep. At any rate, she's quit doing the work. Pretty soon she has another kid. J.P.'s in his mid-twenties by now. He's buying a house. He says he was happy with his life. "I was happy with the way things were going," he says. "I had everything I wanted. I had a wife and kids I loved, and I was doing what I wanted to do with my life." But for some reason—who knows why we do what we do?—his drinking picks up. For a long time he drinks beer and beer only. Any kind of beer—it didn't matter. He says he could drink beer twenty-four hours a day. He'd drink beer at night while he watched TV. Sure, once in a while he drank hard stuff. But that was only if they went out on the town, which was not often, or else when they had company over. Then a time comes, he doesn't know why, when he makes the switch from beer to gin-and-tonic. And he'd have more gin-and-tonic after dinner, sitting in front of the TV. There was always a glass of gin-and-tonic in his hand. He says he actually liked the taste of it. He began stopping off after work for drinks before he went home to have more drinks. Then he began missing some dinners. He just wouldn't show up. Or else he'd show up, but he wouldn't want any-thing to eat. He'd filled up on snacks at the bar. Sometimes he'd walk in the door and for no good reason throw his lunch pail across the living room. When Roxy yelled at him, he'd turn around and go out again. He moved his drinking time up to early afternoon, while he was still supposed to be working. He tells me that he was starting off the morning with a couple of drinks. He'd have a belt of the stuff before he brushed his teeth. Then he'd have his coffee. He'd go to work with a thermos bottle of vodka in his lunch pail.

J.P. quits talking. He just clams up. What's going on? I'm listening. It's helping me relax, for one thing. It's taking me away from my own situation. After a minute, I say, "What the hell? Go on, J.P." He's pulling his chin. But pretty soon he starts talking again.

J.P. and Roxy are having some real fights now. I mean *fights*. J.P. says that one time she hit him in the face with her fist and broke his nose. "Look at this," he says. "Right here." He shows me a line across the bridge of his nose. "That's a broken nose." He returned the favor. He dislocated her shoulder for her. Another time he split her lip. They beat on each other in front of the kids. Things got out of hand. But he kept on drinking. He couldn't stop. And nothing could make him stop. Not even with Roxy's dad and her brother threatening to beat the hell out of him. They told Roxy she should take the kids and clear out. But Roxy said it was her problem. She got herself into it, and she'd solve it.

Now J.P. gets real quiet again. He hunches his shoulders and pulls down in his chair. He watches a car driving down the road between this place and the hills.

I say, "I want to hear the rest of this, J.P. You better keep talking."

"I just don't know," he says. He shrugs.

"It's all right," I say. And I mean it's okay for him to tell it. "Go on, J.P."

One way she tried to fix things, J.P. says, was by finding a boyfriend. J.P. would like to know how she found the time with the house and kids.

I look at him and I'm surprised. He's a grown man. "If you want to do that," I say, "you find the time. You make the time."

J.P. shakes his head. "I guess so," he says.

Anyway, he found out about it—about Roxy's boyfriend—and he went wild. He manages to get Roxy's wedding ring off her finger. And when he does, he cuts it into several pieces with a pair of wire-cutters. Good, solid fun. They'd already gone a couple of rounds on this occasion. On his way to work the next morning, he gets arrested on a drunk charge. He loses his driver's license. He can't drive the truck to work anymore. Just as well, he says. He'd already fallen off a roof the week before and broken his thumb. It was just a matter of time until he broke his neck, he says.

* * * * *

He was here at Frank Martin's to dry out and to figure how to get his life back on track. But he wasn't here against his will, any more than I was. We weren't locked up. We could leave any time we wanted. But a minimum stay of a week was recommended, and two weeks or a month was, as they put it, "strongly advised."

As I said, this is my second time at Frank Martin's. When I was trying to sign a check to pay in advance for a week's stay, Frank Martin said, "The holidays are always bad. Maybe you should think of sticking around a little longer this time? Think in terms of a couple of weeks. Can you do a couple of weeks? Think about it, anyway. You don't have to decide anything right now," he said. He held his thumb on the check and I signed my name. Then I walked my girlfriend to the front door and said goodbye. "Goodbye," she said, and she lurched into the doorjamb and then onto the porch. It's late afternoon. It's raining. I go from the door to the window. I move the curtain and watch her drive away. She's in my car. She's drunk. But I'm drunk, too, and there's nothing I can do. I make it to a big chair that's close to the radiator, and I sit down. Some guys look up from their TV. Then they shift back to what they were watching. I just sit there. Now and then I look up at something that's happening on the screen.

Later that afternoon the front door banged open and J.P. was brought in between these two big guys—his father-in-law and brother-in-law, I find out afterward. They steered J.P. across the room. The old guy signed him in and gave Frank Martin a check. Then these two guys helped J.P. upstairs. I guess they put him to bed. Pretty soon the old guy and the other guy came downstairs and headed for the front door. They couldn't seem to get out of this place fast enough. It was like they couldn't wait to wash their hands of all this. I didn't blame them. Hell, no. I don't know how I'd act if I was in their shoes.

A day and a half later J.P. and I meet up on the front porch. We shake hands and comment on the weather. J.P. has a case of the shakes. We sit down and prop our feet up on the railing. We lean back in our chairs like we're just out there taking our ease, like we might be getting ready to talk about our bird dogs. That's when J.P. gets going with his story.

* * * * *

It's cold out, but not too cold. It's a little overcast. Frank Martin comes outside to finish his cigar. He has on a sweater buttoned all the way up. Frank Martin is short and heavy-set. He has curly gray hair and a small head. His head is too small for the rest of his body. Frank Martin puts the cigar in his mouth and stands with his arms crossed over his chest. He works that cigar in his mouth and looks across the valley. He stands there like a prizefighter, like somebody who knows the score.

J.P. gets quiet again. I mean, he's hardly breathing. I toss my cigarette into the coal bucket and look hard at J.P., who scoots farther down in his chair. J.P. pulls up his collar. What the hell's going on? I wonder. Frank Martin uncrosses his arms and takes a puff on the cigar. He lets the smoke carry out of his mouth. Then he raises his chin toward the hills and says, "Jack London used to have a big place on the other side of this valley. Right over there behind that green hill you're looking at. But alcohol killed him. Let that be a lesson to you. He was a better man than any of us. But he couldn't handle the stuff, either." Frank Martin looks at what's left of his cigar. It's gone out. He tosses it into the bucket. "You guys want to read something while you're here, read that book of his, *The Call of the Wild*. You know the one I'm talking about? We have it inside if you want to read something. It's about this animal that's half dog and half wolf. End of sermon," he says, and then hitches his pants up and tugs his sweater down. "I'm going inside," he says. "See you at lunch."

"I feel like a bug when he's around," J.P. says. "He makes me feel like a bug." J.P. shakes his head. Then he says, "Jack London. What a name! I wish I had me a name like that. Instead of the name I got."

* * * * *

My wife brought me up here the first time. That's when we were still together, trying to make things work out. She brought me here and she stayed around for an hour or two, talking to Frank Martin in private. Then she left. The next morning Frank Martin got me aside and said, "We can help you. If you want help and want to listen to what we say." But I didn't know if they could help me or not. Part of me wanted help. But there was another part.

This time around, it was my girlfriend who drove me here. She was driving my car. She drove us through a rainstorm. We drank champagne all the way. We were both drunk when she pulled up in the drive. She intended to drop me off, turn around, and drive home again. She had things to do. One thing she had to do was to go to work the next day. She was a secretary. She had an okay job with this electronic-parts firm. She also had this mouthy teenaged son. I wanted her to get a room in town, spend the night, and then drive home. I don't know if she got the room or not. I haven't heard from her since she led me up the front steps the other day and walked me into Frank Martin's office and said, "Guess who's here."

But I wasn't mad at her. In the first place, she didn't have any idea what she was letting herself in for when she said I could stay with her after my wife asked me to leave. I felt sorry for her. The reason I felt sorry for her was that on the day before Christmas her Pap smear came back, and the news was not cheery. She'd have to go back to the doctor, and real soon. That kind of news was reason enough for both of us to start drinking. So what we did was get ourselves good and drunk. And on Christmas Day we were still drunk. We had to go out to a restaurant to eat, because she didn't feel like cooking. The two of us and her mouthy teenaged son opened some presents, and then we went to this steakhouse near her apartment. I wasn't hungry. I had some soup and a hot roll. I drank a bottle of wine with the soup. She drank some wine, too. Then we started in on Bloody Marys. For the next couple of days, I didn't eat anything except salted nuts. But I drank a lot of bourbon. Then I said to her, "Sugar, I think I'd better pack up. I better go back to Frank Martin's."

She tried to explain to her son that she was going to be gone for a while and he'd have to get his own food. But right as we were going out the door, this mouthy kid screamed at us. He screamed, "The hell with you! I hope you never come back. I hope you kill yourselves!" Imagine this kid!

Before we left town, I had her stop at the package store, where I bought us the champagne. We stopped someplace else for plastic glasses. Then we picked up a bucket of fried chicken. We set out for Frank Martin's in this rainstorm, drinking and listening to music. She drove. I looked after the radio and poured. We tried to make a little party of it. But we were sad, too. There was that fried chicken, but we didn't eat any.

I guess she got home okay. I think I would have heard something if she didn't. But she hasn't called me, and I haven't called her. Maybe she's had some news about herself by now. Then again, maybe she hasn't heard anything. Maybe it was all a mistake. Maybe it was somebody else's smear. But she has my car, and I have things at her house. I know we'll be seeing each other again.

They clang an old farm bell here to call you for mealtime. J.P. and I get out of our chairs and we go inside. It's starting to get too cold on the porch, anyway. We can see our breath drifting out from us as we talk.

* * * * *

New Year's Eve morning I try to call my wife. There's no answer. It's okay. But even if it wasn't okay, what am I supposed to do? The last time we talked on the phone, a couple of weeks ago, we screamed at each other. I hung a few names on her. "Wet brain!" she said, and put the phone back where it belonged.

But I wanted to talk to her now. Something had to be done about my stuff. I still had things at her house, too.

One of the guys here is a guy who travels. He goes to Europe and places. That's what he says, anyway. Business, he says. He also says he has his drinking under control and he doesn't have any idea why he's here at Frank Martin's. But he doesn't remember getting here. He laughs about it, about his not remembering. "Anyone can have a blackout," he says. "That doesn't prove a thing." He's not a drunk—he tells us this and we listen. "That's a serious charge to make," he says. "That kind of talk can ruin a good man's prospects." He says that if he'd only stick to whiskey and water, no ice, he'd never have these blackouts. It's the ice they put into your drink that does it. "Who do you know in Egypt?" he asks me. "I can use a few names over there."

For New Year's Eve dinner Frank Martin serves steak and baked potato. My appetite's coming back. I clean up everything on my plate and I could eat more. I look over at Tiny's plate. Hell, he's hardly touched a thing. His steak is just sitting there. Tiny is not the same old Tiny. The poor bastard had planned to be at home tonight. He'd planned to be in his robe and slippers in front of the TV, holding hands with his wife. Now he's afraid to leave. I can understand. One seizure means you're ready for another. Tiny hasn't told any more nutty stories on himself since it happened. He's stayed quiet and kept to himself. I ask him if I can have his steak, and he pushes his plate over to me.

Some of us are still up, sitting around the TV, watching Times Square, when Frank Martin comes in to show us his cake. He brings it around and shows it to each of us. I know he didn't make it. It's just a bakery cake. But it's still a cake. It's a big white cake. Across the top there's writing in pink letters. The writing says, HAPPY NEW YEAR—ONE DAY AT A TIME.

"I don't want any stupid cake," says the guy who goes to Europe and places. "Where's the champagne?" he says, and laughs.

We all go into the dining room. Frank Martin cuts the cake. I sit next to J.P.

J.P. eats two pieces and drinks a Coke. I eat a piece and wrap another piece in a napkin, thinking of later.

J.P. lights a cigarette—his hands are steady now—and he tells me his wife is coming in the morning, the first day of the new year.

"That's great," I say. I nod. I lick the frosting off my finger. "That's good news, J.P."

"I'll introduce you," he says.

"I look forward to it," I say.

We say goodnight. We say Happy New Year. I use a napkin on my fingers. We shake hands.

I go to the phone, put in a dime, and call my wife collect. But nobody answers this time, either. I think about calling my girlfriend, and I'm dialing her number when I realize I really don't want to talk to her. She's probably at home watching the same thing on TV that I've been watching. Anyway, I don't want to talk to her. I hope she's okay. But if she has something wrong with her, I don't want to know about it.

* * * * *

After breakfast, J.P. and I take coffee out to the porch. The sky is clear, but it's cold enough for sweaters and jackets.

"She asked me if she should bring the kids," J.P. says. "I told her she should keep the kids at home. Can you imagine? My God, I don't want my kids up here."

We use the coal bucket for an ashtray. We look across the valley to where Jack London used to live. We're drinking more coffee when this car turns off the road and comes down the drive.

"That's her!" J.P. says. He puts his cup next to his chair. He gets up and goes down the steps.

I see this woman stop the car and set the brake. I see J.P. open the door. I watch her get out, and I see them hug each other. I look away. Then I look back. J.P. takes her by the arm and they come up the stairs. This woman broke a man's nose once. She has had two kids, and much trouble, but she loves this man who has her by the arm. I get up from the chair.

"This is my friend," J.P. says to his wife. "Hey, this is Roxy."

Roxy takes my hand. She's a tall, good-looking woman in a knit cap. She has on a coat, a heavy sweater, and slacks. I recall what J.P. told me about the boyfriend and the wire-cutters. I don't see any wedding ring. That's in pieces somewhere, I guess. Her hands are broad and the fingers have these big knuckles. This is a woman who can make fists if she has to.

"I've heard about you," I say. "J.P. told me how you got acquainted. Something about a chimney, J.P. said."

"Yes, a chimney," she says. "There's probably a lot else he didn't tell you," she says. "I bet he didn't tell you everything," she says, and laughs. Then—she can't wait any longer—she slips her arm around J.P. and kisses him on the cheek. They start to move to the door. "Nice meeting you," she says. "Hey, did he tell you he's the best sweep in the business?"

"Come on now, Roxy," J.P. says. He has his hand on the doorknob.

"He told me he learned everything he knew from you," I say.

"Well, that much is sure true," she says. She laughs again. But it's like she's thinking about something else. J.P. turns the doorknob. Roxy lays her hand over his. "Joe, can't we go into town for lunch? Can't I take you someplace?"

J.P. clears his throat. He says, "It hasn't been a week yet." He takes his hand off the doorknob and brings his fingers to his chin. "I think they'd like it if I didn't leave the place for a little while yet. We can have some coffee here," he says.

"That's fine," she says. Her eyes work over to me again. "I'm glad Joe's made a friend. Nice to meet you," she says.

They start to go inside. I know it's a dumb thing to do, but I do it anyway. "Roxy," I say. And they stop in the doorway and look at me. "I need some luck," I say. "No kidding. I could do with a kiss myself."

J.P. looks down. He's still holding the knob, even though the door is open. He turns the knob back and forth. But I keep looking at her. Roxy grins. "I'm not a sweep anymore," she says. "Not for years. Didn't Joe tell you that? But, sure, I'll kiss you, sure."

She moves over. She takes me by the shoulders—I'm a big man—and she plants this kiss on my lips. "How's that?" she says.

"That's fine," I say.

"Nothing to it," she says. She's still holding me by the shoulders. She's looking me right in the eyes. "Good luck," she says, and then she lets go of me.

"See you later, pal," J.P. says. He opens the door all the way, and they go in.

I sit down on the front steps and light a cigarette. I watch what my hand does, then I blow out the match. I've got the shakes. I started out with them this morning. This morning I wanted something to drink. It's depressing, but I didn't say anything about it to J.P. I try to put my mind on something else.

I'm thinking about chimney sweeps—all that stuff I heard from J.P.—when for some reason I start to think about a house my wife and I once lived in. That house didn't have a chimney, so I don't know what makes me remember it now. But I remember the house and how we'd only been in there a few weeks when I heard a noise outside one morning. It was Sunday morning and it was still dark in the bedroom. But there was this pale light coming in from the bedroom window. I listened. I could hear something scrape against the side of the house. I jumped out of bed and went to look.

"My God!" my wife says, sitting up in bed and shaking the hair away from her face. Then she starts to laugh. "It's Mr. Venturini," she says. "I forgot to tell you. He said he was coming to paint the house today. Early. Before it gets too hot. I forgot all about it," she says, and laughs. "Come back to bed, honey. It's just him."

"In a minute," I say.

I push the curtain away from the window. Outside, this old guy in white coveralls is standing next to his ladder. The sun is just starting to break above the mountains. The old guy and I look each other over. It's the landlord, all right—this old guy in coveralls. But his coveralls are too big for him. He needs a shave, too. And he's wearing this baseball cap to cover his bald head. Goddam it, I think, if he isn't a weird old fellow. And a wave of happiness comes over me that I'm not him—that I'm me and that I'm inside this bedroom with my wife.

He jerks his thumb toward the sun. He pretends to wipe his forehead. He's letting me know he doesn't have all that much time. The old fart breaks into a grin. It's then I realize I'm naked. I look down at myself. I look at him again and shrug. What did he expect?

My wife laughs. "Come on," she says. "Get back in this bed. Right now. This minute. Come on back to bed."

I let go of the curtain. But I keep standing there at the window. I can see the old fellow nod to himself like he's saying, "Go on, sonny, go back to bed. I understand." He tugs on the bill of his cap. Then he sets about his business. He picks up his bucket. He starts climbing the ladder.

* * * * *

I lean back into the step behind me now and cross one leg over the other. Maybe later this afternoon I'll try calling my wife again. And then I'll call to see what's happening with my girlfriend. But I don't want to get her mouthy kid on the line. If I do call, I hope he'll be out somewhere doing whatever he does when he's not around the house. I try to remember if I ever read any Jack London books. I can't remember. But there was a story of his I read in high school. "To Build a Fire," it was called. This guy in the Yukon is freezing. Imagine it—he's actually going to freeze to death if he can't get a fire going. With a fire, he can dry his socks and things and warm himself.

He gets his fire going, but then something happens to it. A branchful of snow drops on it. It goes out. Meanwhile, it's getting colder. Night is coming on.

I bring some change out of my pocket. I'll try my wife first. If she answers, I'll wish her a Happy New Year. But that's it. I won't bring up business. I won't raise my voice. Not even if she starts something. She'll ask me where I'm calling from, and I'll have to tell her. I won't say anything about New Year's resolutions. There's no way to make a joke out of this. After I talk to her, I'll call my girlfriend. Maybe I'll call her first. I'll just have to hope I don't get her kid on the line. "Hello, sugar," I'll say when she answers. "It's me."

SLAVE DRIVER

WANDA COLEMAN

Trudy recognized them immediately, three silver-haired gents—father, uncle, son, all regular patients—as they entered the central-city doctor's office that evening. They were small men, businessmen, originally from Eastern Europe, proud shrewds radiating the arrogance of acquired American wealth. Clad in casually elegant sweaters, slacks, loafers, they looked frail, obviously feeling changes the clock had wrought. Even the son was well into his sixties.

Trudy's stomach tightened. As the front office receptionist and back office general worker, she would greet them stoically, if not enthusiastically, but could not help but anticipate the moment when their assault would begin.

The son and uncle struggled as they dragged August, the father, through the outer door into the lobby. He was past ninety and, as far as Trudy was concerned, as evil as he was platinum-haired. He had made it a ritual to insult her. He did so freely in front of Mona, the Japanese office manager, knowing that she would keep quiet. No one sane would risk gainful employment defending a nigger, went the implication.

Trudy never challenged Mona's silence. Together, they manned the physicians' front office counter and examination prep area. As a child, Mona had survived internment in one of the stateside camps of World War II. Her family lost everything. Mona still had the disturbing habit, Trudy observed, of never throwing away uneaten food. Her desk drawer was filled with stale packets of cookies and gritty candy bars. She would keep leftover fruit from lunch on the counter until it blackened with rot or whitened with mold.

There was nothing in the way of friendship between them. Not even the neutral pop-culture chitchat that usually bridges that treacherous void between workers of different social stripes. Trudy had tried to no avail.

She made mental notes of instances when a patient cracked a racist joke or made an ugly comment in front of them. Mona's back would stiffen, but she never said a word—of reproach to the patient, or in empathy to Trudy afterward. Trudy weathered every difficulty, except those presented by August and his kinfolk.

Last time, August actually called her a "colored wench." She had gone hot and cold. She had fought to keep from snatching the reprobate through the reception window and blessing him with every pound of her strength. Her eyes had begun to tear in repressed rage. Her hands had trembled as she mentally forced the faces of her children into view, envisioning what it would mean to them if she ended up in jail on charges of assault. She left old August smirking as he stood at the window, went to the back of the building and remained there.

Mona had come in and had seen August sitting quietly on one of the sofas.

"Are you being helped?" she had asked.

He had smiled and shrugged.

She then unlocked the inner office door, saw the reception area was untended and went around back. Trudy was sitting behind the back office counter, typing away at the day's dictation, earphones in her ear.

Mona had rapped loudly on the counter. Trudy looked up. It was hard enough to be unappreciated by her employers, difficult enough to bear Mona's warped indifference, but excruciating to endure repeated abuse from their aging, well-to-do clientele. Trudy had battled to maintain her mask of front-office decorum. It continually galled her that this was something Mona failed to understand.

"Why are you back here, when there's a patient up front?"

Trudy looked at her and said nothing. Mona cocked her head.

"Are you all right?"

"No," Trudy said, "I'm not all right."

"Aren't you going back up front?"

Trudy stared at her without offering an answer.

Mona looked at her blankly and shrugged. "I swear, I don't know what's wrong with you people."

* * * * *

Now, in unspoken protest, whenever Trudy spotted a troublesome patient coming into the office, she abandoned the counter without a word, and went around to the station in back, leaving them to Mona. But on this visit, Mona was out running errands for the doctors, and the lab technician—a recent arrival from Palestine— was analyzing the morning's urine specimens. Trudy had no choice but to cope with the trio.

August's son, a willowy man, looked as if he were going to snap under his father's weight. Trudy was struck by how docile and infirm August had become. The uncle closed the front office door with his foot. Then the two younger men labored to get August onto the waiting room sofa where he lay breathlessly moaning as the uncle approached the reception window and glared defensively at Trudy.

"We don't have an appointment," he said anxiously. "Think the doc'll see him?"

"Sure," her bright smile was phony.

Trudy went to the physicians' chambers, knocked on the door, and informed the doctor on call that he had an emergency patient. She alerted the technician that tests might be needed, then quickly prepared an examination room. That done, she returned to the inner office door, invited the men in. Again they wrestled with August, bouncing him against the waiting room sofa until they managed to pull him to his feet. Unable to budge him any farther, they stood there, staring at her blankly.

"We can't lift him," the son said softly. "And he can't walk."

She heard the exquisite pain in his words. The anguish in his face was mirrored in the silent frown of the uncle. Three old men. This was relentless recognition, a profound admission of diminished manhood—their notions of manhood. She could not help but respect their pain.

"Here, let me help." She said it so sweetly she could hardly stand herself. She imagined herself rising above their level of bigotry. They had treated her very nastily, especially the crusty old August, who went out of his way to demean her. And they knew she knew it was because she was black. She had never complained to any of the doctors. The physicians she worked for were white men themselves, immigrants and the sons of immigrants. Without discussion, it was understood that no matter how liberal in their hiring practices—at root—they basically shared August's contempt for the African American.

* * * * *

Trudy had resisted temptation to return the abuse she was subjected to, ever mindful of how badly she needed to keep her job in order to care for her children. An economic recession was on and, nationwide, decent-paying alternatives were scarce. She liked her job and had no desire to quit, as said to friends, "behind the racist bullshit of busybodies."

What the immigrants didn't know was that Trudy could drive herself far harsher than any so-called boss. It was she who insisted that her ghetto apartment sparkle as if it were a mansion, dusting and polishing everything that could be dusted and polished. It was she—in the role of mother and father—who fed and clothed her children, washed and ironed the laundry, shopped for groceries, washed and waxed the car, paid all the debts. It was she alone who minded the children, drove back and forth from school to babysitter, and scheduled what entertainment was affordable in her efforts to give them a decent life. It was she who spent loveless night after night addressing envelopes by hand, for a mail order outfit, to earn extra money—after the kids were asleep.

She believed she could make time her ally by finding the cheapest clock with the loudest alarm. She set it religiously after midnight before she fell into an exhausted sleep. It woke her at four-thirty every morning, allowing her barely enough time to tend to her person, wake and feed the children, get them to school and then begin her thankless workday anew.

First to arrive every morning, before making the coffee and taking messages from the answering service, she brought in the daily newspaper, one she'd take home each night to glance at before bedtime in concert with the TV news. The headlines invariably left her numb and deepened her sleep. She had few opinions about anything that could not be reduced to an elemental right or wrong. Keeping up with local politics was impossible beyond noting the skin color of the candidate for whom she might vote. Headlines that thundered the unilateral invasion of a country to send strident messages to enemy nations concerned her only to the extent that one of her kinfolk had joined the military.

Otherwise, fear and frustration defined her dreams. They were the dreams of a statistic she knew uncomfortably well: working class poor, single mother.

It was she who spent any available waking moment wondering what she could do to escape poverty, wondering what it would take to free herself and her children from its misery. She counted those neighbors who fell around her, families destroyed, lives taken, knowing it was only a matter of time before she, too—and her children—became victims of some inevitable violence. Too often she had stood among onlookers when a lover or spouse was taken away in handcuffs; or carried oven-fresh casserole dishes to bereaved families following the gang-related funeral of a child or teenager. Nightly, she listened as police helicopters swooped over rooftops, as sirens and shouts echoed up and down the block.

All I have is my high school diploma and my back.

The dread drove her so fiercely that it spilled over into her workplace, manifested as compulsive neatness, resulting in a medical office where every chart, desk, file, and ledger was in perfect order. She did the billing, made appointments, transcribed dictation, assisted the laboratory technician and the office manager, was Janeofall.

The white man hadn't been born, she thought, who could drive her one centesimal harder.

* * * * *

Trudy positioned herself at August's side, pausing briefly to cushion his apparent shock at being touched by a large ebony woman for the first time in his life. Trudy was dark-skinned, a full six-feet in height and weighed a firm, high-busted two hundred pounds. Her thighs were thick, her legs sturdy. Opening her arms, she cradled August as if he were a slightly hefty infant.

He looked at her with grateful amazement.

She was surprised at how light he was as she carried him through the waiting-room door.

The son and uncle followed. They watched helplessly as Trudy lowered August onto the examination table, handed them a paper dressing gown, and instructed them to undress him to his waist. The three men stared at her, gasping, hands and fingers twitching in befuddlement.

"You're a strong one, aren't you," the uncle finally muttered.

Appreciating the complexities of embarrassment and tarnished masculine pride, she tried to offer some simple explanation to defuse the situation, perhaps break their spell of wounded self-esteem.

"My father was a boxer back in the '40s and '50s. When I was little, I used to work out with him during training sessions."

"Oh," August nodded. The men smiled at one another awkwardly.

Trudy left them in the doctor's care and returned to her front office duties. Almost as soon as she sat down, consternation set in. She realized that they had accepted her explanation about her father because it played into the stereotype of the Negro as superior work animal.

Mona finally came and relieved Trudy, who avoided the geriatric trio the rest of that evening, working at the back desk until August was rolled from the office in a wheelchair.

* * * * *

A month later, during lunch break, the reception window quietly slid back, pushed open from the waiting room side. Old man August stuck his head and hands through the opening. It was his first visit since Trudy had carried him into the examination room. He stared at her without a hello.

Mona was across the street at the hospital cafeteria. As usual, Trudy ate while on duty. She neatly put her lunch aside and smiled at August warmly, recalling how sick he'd been. She wiped her hands thoroughly and rose from the counter to face him at the window.

He had recovered. His eyes sparked with mischief. In his hand was a slip of paper she recognized as the bill she had prepared and sent. It dangled loosely in one ancient, liverspotted paw, just within reach.

"Let me talk to the doctor!" he barked in her face, brusqueness underscored by his thick-tongued accent.

Trudy sighed. August was up to his old wickedness. He was familiar with the office routine and knew the doctors were out on lunch break. Yet he demanded she be put through paces.

"The doctor is at lunch," she repeated stoically, trying to echo her former sweetness, "as you well know."

"I SAID I WANT TO SEE HIM!" August roared.

The invoice fluttered loosely in his hand.

"If there's a question about the bill, perhaps I can help," she said as she reached for it. August snappily withdrew it from the window.

"YOU?" He snorted it like a dirty word. "You help me?" He trumpeted like a bull elephant. "You—you're just the SCULLERY MAID around here!"

Instantly, her eyes glassed over.

She fought herself to keep still. Her mouth opened, her jaw hinged and unhinged but no sound came forth. Her nose began to run, and dripped down onto her smock. She did not dare move a whit, and did not raise a hand to wipe it clean, teetering before her tormentor, frozen with rage.

His eyes laughed in her fury.

The click of the back-office door, followed by the rustle of a skirt and the soft padding of Mona's feet, brought her out of the trance. Mona peeped around her, through the service window, trying to see what she was staring at. Her eyes swept the waiting room.

August was gone.

Oblivious to Trudy's state, Mona glanced down at the counter and saw the unfinished lunch nesting between the phone bank and the appointment book.

"You take that around back and finish up," Mona snapped.

"My name is Trudy," she snapped back. "T-r-u-d-y. And I like to hear it said."

OUT OF THE SNOW

ANDRE DUBUS

On a dark winter morning, upstairs in her new home, LuAnn woke to classical piano on the clock radio; she was in her forty-fourth year, she had a few strands of gray in her long black hair, and this was her eighty-third day without smoking; before opening her eyes she remembered dreaming in the night of a red-and-white package of cigarettes. Then she looked at Ted limping naked to the closet. He was a big man; the sideburns of his brown beard were gray. His knee had been shattered and torn by shrapnel when he was nineteen in Vietnam, and it would not completely bend, and often it was painful. She turned off the radio, and in the silence she could feel her children sleeping; it was as though she heard their breath and saw their faces on pillows. She stood, wearing a white gown, and started to make the bed, and Ted in his burgundy robe came to help, and she remembered last night's lovemaking, and watched him smoothing the blue satin comforter. She said: "I dreamed of cigarettes last night."

"That isn't fair."

"I'd love one now, with coffee."

"So would I."

"Great. Is that why I'm doing this? So eighteen years from now I'll want to smoke?"

His blue eyes watched her. That is what he did most of the time, when she was angry or sad or frightened: watched her and listened. He had told her he stopped believing in advice years before he met her, or stopped believing people wanted advice; they wanted to be looked at and heard by someone who loved them. She said: "Nice night, Ted."

"Yes." He smiled. "Nice night, LuAnn."

He went to the bathroom at the far end of the hall, and she went to the one she shared with Julia and Elizabeth. She put on makeup, and in the bedroom she dressed in jeans and a green turtleneck and high black boots. Then she went to the children's rooms and woke them by placing a hand on their shoulders: Julia, her first child, who was ten, then Elizabeth, then Sam, lying among stuffed bears. She always woke them gently because she felt she was pulling them from childhood. They were dark-haired, sleepy, and slow to dress. She knew they were slow because they were reluctant, but there was something more, something she wanted to acquire; they were slow in summer, too, dressing for the beach. Hurry was imposed on them by adults; they had not lived long enough to see time as something they should control, long enough to believe they could. LuAnn had taken maternity leave to give birth to Julia, and had not gone back to her job. She had been the publicity director of a small publisher in Boston. Two years later Elizabeth was born, and after another two Sam, and by then LuAnn knew what these children knew: they ate when they were hungry, slept when they were tired, and looked at the present with curiosity. She was trying to focus on the present now, as she went downstairs, aware of her breathing, her leg muscles, the smell of coffee, the electric light in the dining room and twilight in the living room; and wanting to smoke, then calling over her shoulder to the children to hurry.

In the kitchen, Ted stood with his cane, pouring coffee; he wore his blue double-breasted suit and a red tie with a pale blue shirt. He was flying to Baltimore to take a deposition and would stay there for the night. He had brought in the newspaper from the box at the end of their long driveway that curved downhill through trees. He put a spoon of sugar and some hot milk from a pot in her coffee, then handed it to her. He stood resting on his cane as she took her first sip; then with a finger he touched her knuckles at the handle of the cup, and bent down and gave her a quick kiss; his throat and his cheeks above his beard smelled of aftershave lotion, and she breathed that with the aroma of coffee and said: "You're not bad, Ted Briggs."

"Neither are you, Ms. Arceneaux."

She went through the mudroom, where boots were on benches and coats hung on pegs, and stepped outside, and smelled snow in the air. The evergreens were still black and the sky was dark gray. She breathed deeply into her stomach and looked up at the sky and raised her arms. She went back into the light of the kitchen; upstairs the children's steps were slow but steady, so she did not call to them. Ted was making sandwiches at the counter. She took three grapefruit from the refrigerator and stood beside him and sliced the grapefruit in halves, then cut their sections from the rind. She drank coffee and poured measuring cups of water into a pot. Until eighty-three days ago she had waked herself each morning for twenty-six years with coffee and cigarettes. Her flesh could not remember what it had felt, waking without wanting those. She stepped to the sink and poured out her coffee, then spread butter on eight slices of bread, and margarine on two. Ted's cholesterol was high, and she obeyed the rules about that, and imposed them on him; she ate what she wanted to, and she did not give margarine to the children because she did not trust it, suspecting that decades from now it would attack them in ways no one had predicted. She sprinkled brown sugar on the bread, then cinnamon, and looked at Ted's profile and said: "You could cheat tonight, you know. Have yourself a great dinner."

"I plan to."

She wondered if she had really been talking about food, then knew that she was, and it had reminded her of adultery. Once she had nearly cheated, and she had learned how simple and even negligible it could be, making love with someone else while loving your husband; and since then she had known it could happen to Ted, as easily as a tire blowing out, or a bluefish striking his hook. She had told none of this to him; she had told Marsha and had confessed to a priest that in her heart she had been unfaithful, though not with her body.

He sliced the sandwiches in triangular halves, wrapped them in waxed paper, and placed them in the three lunch boxes. They were red, blue, yellow. He wrapped cookies and put in each box an apple and a tangerine. She imagined him tonight eating pâté and duck, and herself in the living room, after the children were asleep, smoking cigarettes. She looked at the clock and was about to call the children, knowing her voice would be high and tense, but then she heard them on the stairs. They came into the dining room, Julia and Elizabeth murmuring, Sam gazing, seeing something in his mind that was nowhere in the room. She quietly marveled at these little people: they were dressed; they wore shoes; their hair was brushed. Probably their beds were made. She sat with them and Ted and ate grapefruit. Then she boiled the water in the pot, measured oatmeal into it, and watched it boil again, then lowered the flame. She slid the pan of cinnamon bread into the oven, left the door partially open, and turned on the broiler.

Her mind was eluding her: it was living the day ahead of her; it was in the aisle of the supermarket, it was bringing the groceries into the house and putting them away; it was driving to the gym for aerobics and weight training; it was home eating lunch, then taking clothes to the dry cleaners and getting the clothes that were there, and driving home before three-forty when the school bus brought the children to the driveway; it was lighting charcoal in the grill on the sundeck. Maybe snow would be falling then; she loved cooking in the snow. She had a housekeeper three days a week and she liked running the household. None of it absorbed her fully enough to imprison her mind, as some work in school and some at the publishing house had. So freedom was both her challenge and her vocation: she was free on most days and nights to concentrate fully on the moment at hand, and this was far more difficult than performing work she had been assigned as a student for sixteen years, and a worker for eleven. She had told Ted she must learn to be five again, before time began to mean what one could produce in its passing; or to be like St. Thérèse of Lisieux, who knew so young that the essence of life was in the simplest of tasks, and in the kindness to the people in your life. Watching the brown sugar bubbling in the light of the flames, smelling it and the cinnamon, and listening to her family talking about snow, she told herself that this toast and oatmeal were a sacrament, the physical form that love assumed in this moment, as last night's lovemaking was, as most of her actions were. When she was able to remember this and concentrate on it, she knew the significance of what she was doing; as now, using a pot holder, she drew the pan from the oven, then spooned oatmeal into bowls her family came from the dining room to receive from her hands.

At seven forty-five the children put on parkas and gloves; Sam wore a ski cap, and the girls kept theirs in their pockets. They carried book bags and lunch boxes and LuAnn and Ted went outside with them, kissed them, and watched them walking down the dark asphalt drive, till it curved around pines and they were out of sight. She cleared the table and Ted rinsed things and put them in the dishwasher. He went upstairs, then came down wearing a dark blue overcoat, his cane in his right hand, his left holding a small suitcase and his briefcase. She took the briefcase and, without a coat, carried it out to his car in the garage and said: "Call me."

"I will."

"I hate airplanes."

"It'll be fine."

Two images pierced her: Ted in a plane above the earth, and Julia, Elizabeth, and Sam disappearing in the gray light as they rounded the pine trees. She said: "There's so much to fear."

"I know. And we've been lucky."

"I've been thanking God for fear."

"You have?"

"This winter. One afternoon the bus was late with the children. My imagination was like a storm. I stood at the road, and I couldn't get rid of all the terrible pictures. So I started thanking God for this fear, because it meant I love them so much. The sun was shining on the snow and pines, and I stood down there, thinking of what it would be like not to have that fear; not to love anyone so much that you couldn't imagine living on the earth without them." She shivered from the cold, and he held her; her lips were at his throat and she said: "I looked at all that beauty around me, and I was grateful. I was still afraid, but the worst of it went out of me."

He was pressing her against his broad, firm chest. He cried easily and she knew tears were in his eyes now. She kissed him, then stood hugging herself for warmth as he got into the car and backed out of the garage, turning and heading downhill. Before the curve, he waved his arm out the window, and she raised hers; then he was gone.

She went inside, put an Ella Fitzgerald compact disc on in the living room, turned up the volume so she could hear it upstairs, where she looked at the children's beds, smoothed their comforters, picked up socks and underpants on Elizabeth's floor and a nightgown on Julia's, put them in the laundry basket and carried it down to the basement, emptied it into the washing machine, and poured soap on the clothes. She looked out the window at her back lawn: patches of brown grass and old snow, poplars without leaves, and pines. She breathed deeply into her stomach, exhaled singing with Ella, turned on the washing machine, took clothes from the dryer and put them in the basket, and kept singing as she climbed with the basket up the basement and second-floor stairs, and was not winded. Standing at her bed she folded the clothes, then put them in drawers in the three bedrooms. She went downstairs into the music and took out the compact disc and was in the mudroom putting on her beige parka when the phone rang. She answered the one on the kitchen wall, and Marsha said: "Do you have time for lunch after the workout?"

LuAnn heard Marsha inhaling smoke, then blowing it out.

"That sounds wonderful."

"Well, I didn't mean elegant."

"I meant your cigarette. I can have lunch."

"Don't start again. It's not as good as it sounds."

"Easy for you to say."

"If I had half your will, you'd hear me breathing air. You wouldn't even hear me. I'd be that calm."

"Half my fear. I'm going out for groceries."

"Get something sinful."

The market was in a town on the bank of the river, near its mouth at the sea. From her house she drove three miles through wooded country with widely scattered homes. She rolled down her window and let the cold air rush on her face. She did this till her gloved hands were cold and, crossing a bridge over the wide gray river, she rolled up her window, then entered a road where cars moved in single lanes and houses were built close to one another. In the hands of women and men holding steering wheels she saw cigarettes, and she imagined herself very old and strong and alert, one of those gray and wrinkled widows with wonderful eyes. She turned into the shopping center.

In the warm and brightly lit store she slowly pushed a cart. When she was single, and living and working in Boston, she went quickly through stores like this one, snatching cereal and fruit, cookies, cheeses and sliced meat; for dinners she chose food she only had to pour from a can or heat in its package, and she brought home no more than she could carry, walking to her apartment. Often she did not shop till her refrigerator and cupboards were nearly empty. Her best meals were in restaurants with dates or women friends. Then she was married, and she wanted good dinners with Ted. He liked to cook, and on weekends they idly shopped together, and choosing and handling food with him was a new happiness: a flounder lying on ice was no longer a dead fish she must cook before it spoiled; it was part of the earth she and Ted would eat. Now that she was gathering food for Julia and Elizabeth and Sam, too, she saw it in the store as something that would become her children's flesh. As a girl she had learned about the seven sacraments of the Catholic Church, all of them but one administered by a priest; the woman and man gave each other the sacrament of matrimony. Being a mother had taught her that sacraments were her work, and their number was infinite.

As she filled the cart, she looked with compassion at women, the harried ones, some with a child or two, the women who did not have housekeepers and someone to care for their children, perhaps did not have husbands or did not have good ones, who were not going to the gym for a long workout to fulfill and relax them, who had to count the dollars they were spending, whose minds had not received the gifts that she had simply been born with, as she had been born with black hair and French blood; women who as teenagers had gone into the world as bodies and faces with personalities, and so acquired boyfriends, then men, then husbands, and children; they were the women whose work was never done because they could not pay someone else to do at least part of it. No wonder one's voice rose angrily at her small girl riding in the cart, and another grabbed her son's wrist as he reached for a cereal box, and jerked him away from the shelf. The boy's face looked immune. It was not as simple as money, LuAnn knew; it was as complex as the soul. But so often the body ruled, and when it was tired, when it was overwhelmed, venom could spread through the soul. And with money, one could soothe the body, give it rest.

Work was beginning its clandestine assault on Ted's body: he worked too hard and too long. She had liked going to work, had liked being with the people there, and more than the work itself she had liked being an educated woman with a profession; but she had loved none of it, and her happiest moment of the day had been when it ended and she could leave her desk and go out into the world she had felt for eight hours was waiting for her to join it. Ted loved his work, and did it with passion, and if it were taken from him, and if he tried to live as she did, his soul would wither, or implode. If he lost her and the children, his work would not save him. Grief would kill him. She shopped now for the children's bones and teeth, muscles and eyes and skin, and for Ted's arteries; and because he would not be with them tonight, she bought steaks to cook on the grill.

She pushed her full cart to the front of the store, stood in line behind three women at the cashier, and looked out the glass front at the parking lot and the dark sky. No one spoke. She could not hear a voice in the entire store, only the young woman at the register sliding food, and the beeping sound of the computer. Then in another line a child talked and a woman answered; in the aisles behind LuAnn were the voices of children and women, and to her left, among the fruit and vegetables, a man spoke. She leaned on her cart and it moved and she stopped it. She yawned, then looked at the cigarettes stacked in narrow shelves behind the cashier, those packages so soft and light to hold in your hand, so delightful to open and smell. She looked out at the sky, and at the covers of magazines in a rack near the line. She breathed deeply, and the computer beeped, and beeped. She could be alone anywhere without being bored, except in lines of people standing or people in cars, those imposed cessations of motion that drew on her energy more than the motion itself did. She let weight go into her hands on the handle of the cart; her shoulders sagged, and she watched the woman in front of her putting groceries on the counter. Then she glimpsed motion and looked up at the window: snow was falling. The flakes were small and blown at an angle, swirling down among the cars in the parking lot. Standing in electric light, she gazed at its beauty out there under the dark sky, and felt the old and faint dread that was always part of her thrill when she saw falling snow, as though her flesh were born or conceived with its ancestors' knowledge that this windblown white silence could entrap and freeze and kill. On the counter packages slid, and the computer beeped; then it was LuAnn's turn, and as she unloaded the cart, she looked at the young blond woman wearing the store's blue apron and said: "It looks like a storm."

"They say a nor'easter."

"Really?"

"That's what they say."

She looked at the snow. She knew that her house faced northwest and the river flowed southeast, and the market was southeast of her house, and at night she could find the North Star. But how had she become a woman who rarely knew from which direction the wind blew? She said: "I didn't hear the weather report."

"Me neither." The woman was looking down at her work. "They said it in the coffee room."

In the woman's apron pocket was the shape of a cigarette pack. LuAnn said: "Do they let you smoke?"

"We have to go outside."

"I'll turn on the car radio."

The woman looked quizzically at her, and LuAnn smiled and said: "So I'll know what I'm looking at with my own eyes."

The woman smiled, and LuAnn pushed her cart through doors that opened for her, out to the sidewalk, where she looked up at the snow and it landed on her cheeks; when she lowered her face, she saw in her path two approaching young men, both with mustaches, one wearing only a red hooded sweatshirt with his jeans. He looked at her as though he were deciding whether to buy her, and she looked down and swerved the cart around them. They wore work boots. She went to the trunk of her car and put the groceries in it. She turned to push the cart back to the store, and saw the two men standing at its front, watching her. She did not move. Then they did, walking to the left, toward the parking lot. She was afraid, and angry, too, and ashamed of her fear; she pushed the cart to the sidewalk in front of the store, and did not look to her left, where the men had walked. In the car she turned on the windshield wipers and defroster, opened the window, and drove into snow, smelling it and watching it fall. When she crossed the bridge, she looked at the river and the trees on its banks, and two seagulls flying near the water, and snow angling down to the waves. She turned onto the wooded road. It was not time yet for news on the radio; she would call the school or Marsha; if this were a storm, the school would send the children home before the roads got dangerous. A green car was perhaps a quarter of a mile behind her. If the children came home early, she and Marsha could not exercise and go someplace for lunch. At her driveway she turned and climbed the curve and drove into the garage. She opened the trunk and carried two of the bags up the steps and held them with one arm while she unlocked the door and pushed it open, crossed the mudroom, and opened the kitchen door; she put the bags on the counter, went to the answering machine in the dining room, pressed its play button, and listened to Marsha's voice: "The snow is going to stop in early afternoon. There's no snow day. See you at the gym. Let's eat at the Harborside, and have a Manhattan. Remember when people had drinks at lunch?"

A Manhattan: she imagined the stemmed glass, the brown drink, the first good sip. No, not with pretty auburn-haired Marsha, not today. She would take a drag of Marsha's cigarette, to taste and feel that with the whiskey; then she would smoke one. Marsha would protest but would give it to her anyway; then she would smoke another. No, at lunch she would drink water. She put her purse on the dining room table and thought of pushing the barbell up from her chest, exhaling as blood rushed to her muscles. She went into the kitchen, to go outside for more bags of groceries, and two men stepped out of the mudroom, through the open door: the one in the red hooded sweatshirt from the parking lot was in front; behind him was the other man, in a sky blue parka. Her mouth opened, and her body seemed to jump up and back, though her feet did not leave the floor. They had followed her all this way, half an hour from the market; they were doom walking out of the snow. The man in red stopped near the refrigerator, and the one in blue stood beside him; they were close enough to hand something to, if she stepped and reached. They stood between her and the two open doors; she saw falling snow beyond their shoulders and faces, as if it were snow in someone else's life.

She was afraid to turn and run out the front door, or the door to the deck at the other side of the house, or out the back door, down the hall between the playroom and the library; she saw herself running up the hill behind the house, into the woods; running down the sloping front lawn to the road; saw herself dying in the woods and beside the road and on the carpet near the doorway. Her body would not turn its back on them; it knew that if it did, it would die. She was looking at the brown eyes of the one in red; his mustache was brown, he had not shaved today, brown hair curled out from the front of his hood, and his eyes terrified her. There was no fear in them. In their light she saw hatred and anger, and the excitement they gave this man. The other man had darker brown hair and a mustache, and also had not shaved today. Excitement was in his eyes, but not hatred and anger, and she knew he was the follower, the one who would help with and watch whatever happened. Her mouth was still open. She willed it to shape words, utter sounds that would save her. She waited for this, waited for images to form in her mind and become words. But she saw only the eyes of the man in red, and in them she saw herself stripped naked, struck with fists, choked, raped on the floor, both of them raping her; they would take away every bit of her. Now words came to her mind, but not her open mouth: *No, God; not like this.*

Fury rushed with her fear, and she trembled as her soul gathered itself into her blood and muscles. The man in red lifted a hand to his brow and pushed back his hood; his brown curls stirred, and the hood settled behind his neck. Then her left foot was striding quickly forward once, and she watched her right leg and booted foot kicking upward, felt her knee lock before her foot struck the testicles of the man in red. She was amazed; her heart was a flood that filled her chest; she watched his head and torso come forward and down, heard him gasp and groan. Her body was moving, swinging a backhanded left fist at the other man; she saw the one in red fall to his knees and saw her knuckles graze the nose of the one in blue. He pushed her across the room, her back struck the counter near the stove, and he was coming with closed fists and angry eyes. On the counter to her left she saw the teakettle, its copper surface animate, drawing her to it; with her right hand she reached across her body and gripped the handle; she spun to her right, her arm extended, and released the kettle, but his face was gone; the kettle was in the air above his lowered head, then hitting a cabinet. Within the sound of that, she was moving to her left to the skillet on the stove; she grabbed its wooden handle as the kettle hit the floor. She swung backhanded, holding the skillet flat, and its side hit his nose, above his rising hands; blood flowed and she was lifting the skillet with two hands above her head, swinging it to his forehead and the fingers of one hand. His body lowered, his head level now with hers. She hit the top of his head twice; blood was on his mouth and chin and parka, and she felt the man in red to her right; her body was already starting to move toward him as for the third time she hit the head of the man in blue, and he fell.

She leaped to her right: the man in red was on his knees, holding the counter by the refrigerator with his left hand, pulling himself up; his face was pale, and with the anger and hatred in his eyes was pain. She swung the skillet two-handed, from left to right; he lifted his right hand to his face, and with the skillet's bottom she hit his fingers and cheekbone, and knocked his head against the counter. The sound of the blow filled her; the shock of it danced in her. She swung again, hitting his hand and face; and again, smelling blood and saliva from his mouth; then she raised the skillet over her head and hit his brow, and his right hand dropped from his cheek, and his left hand slid off the counter. He was kneeling still; then his head and upper body fell forward, and on the floor his outstretched hands cushioned his face as it hit. He lay bleeding onto the backs of his hands. She looked behind her: the one in blue was on his back now, both hands touching his bleeding nose and lips. She ran to the phone and faced them. They rolled onto their sides, their stomachs, and began pushing themselves up with their arms and legs. She raised the skillet with her right hand and held the phone in her left.

They were crawling away from her. The one in blue stood, weaved once, then bent to the man in red and held his armpits and pulled him upward. The man groaned. Blood was on the floor, and the man in blue had his arm around the waist of the one in red; they went past the refrigerator and into the mudroom. She stood holding the phone and the skillet. They went out the door and down the steps; snow landed on their shoulders and heads. She was breathing fast; the sound of it filled the room. She looked out the doors at snow and, beyond the driveway, a large pine tree. Then she dropped the phone and ran to the steps and stopped. The man in red was in the passenger seat of the car, his hands at his face; the one in blue was starting it. She stood on the top step, holding the skillet with both hands. When the man in blue backed the car and turned it to go downhill, she ran down the steps and stood on snow and read the numbers on the license plate, repeated them aloud as she ran into the mudroom, closed and locked the door, went into the kitchen, closed and locked that door, saying: "Six two seven seven three one."

She faced the door, holding the skillet in her right hand, and picked up the dangling and beeping phone, repeating the license number aloud as her finger pressed nine and one and one.

* * * * *

The two men vanished, and she would never see them again. They remained part of her life: their eyes looking at her before she kicked, and swung the skillet; the feel of her foot striking, and the feel and sound of the skillet hitting skin and bone; the pain in their eyes then; their blood. From the parking lot of the shopping center they had stolen the car they followed her in; they left it at a mall west of her house and stole another, which they left at a hospital in Albany, where they gave names that were probably not theirs and paid cash to have their noses set, then stole a nurse's car that Chicago police found without its tires and radio near the train station.

She told her story first to Ted on the phone, while she waited for the cruiser; then to the young officer who came with the siren on, and whom she asked for a cigarette. He did not smoke. The snow stopped falling while he helped her carry in the groceries. Then she told it to the tall graying detective in a tan overcoat who came to show her photographs of men who broke into houses, and to dust for fingerprints and take samples of blood. He had cigarettes and she smoked and sat at the dining room table and looked at pictures of men whom she had never seen. The detective took off his suit coat and rolled up his sleeves and filled a bucket with hot water, and they kneeled on the floor and with sponges washed the blood from the tile, standing to wring the sponges over the sink. She was doing this when Marsha called from the gym, and she told Marsha the story while the detective emptied the bucket into the sink and began washing it. He gave her a cigarette and left, and Marsha came, trotting from the car, and made tea and gave her cigarettes and LuAnn told her again. Ted phoned to tell her when his flight would arrive in Boston that night; he would be home before the children were in bed, and he was not going to work tomorrow; he was not going to work until they had an alarm system, and its remote control was in her purse.

"In case more than you can handle show up," he said. "*Twenty* guys or so."

Marsha called her husband and told him, and said to come to LuAnn's after work; then she gave LuAnn her cigarettes and left to get her children at school and buy more steaks. At three-thirty LuAnn went outside and looked at snow on the earth and gathered on wide branches of pines. She said: "Thank You." Then she looked up at the gray sky. "That I didn't get killed. That I didn't get raped. That I didn't miss his balls. That I didn't miss with the skillet. That I didn't beg for their mercy. That I didn't kill anyone."

She lowered her face to the earth before her and walked down the driveway and waited for the yellow bus to come around the curve of snow and green and gray trees. When it came, she crouched and hugged Julia and Elizabeth and Sam, and climbed to the house, where in the living room fireplace she stacked logs and started a fire, and they sat on cushions before it, and she told them her story. She stood and showed them how she had kicked, and how she had swung the skillet, her empty hands clenched tightly, her arms quick, and she watched her children's dark and wondering eyes, lit by fire.

Near midnight, the upstairs hall was lighted, all the downstairs rooms were dark, and in front of the burning logs she sat with Ted on cushions. She said: "When I came out of the store and the one in red looked at me the way he did, I looked down. I pushed the cart to the car and put the groceries in the trunk. I was pissed off, but that was going away. I could see the groceries, feel their weight in my hands; feel the snow on my face, and smell it. Then I turned to push the cart back, and they were still there."

She took a cigarette from the second pack Marsha had given her, and looked at Ted's eyes. "I'll quit again tomorrow. This strange sacrament from the earth."

He smiled.

"I've never told you this," she said. "But there's something about taking the cart back instead of leaving it in the parking lot. I don't know when this came to me; it was a few years ago. There's a difference between leaving it where you empty it and taking it back to the front of the store. It's significant."

"Because somebody has to take them in."

"Yes. And if you know that, and you do it for that one guy, you do something else. You join the world. With your body. And for those few moments, you join it with your soul. You move out of your isolation and become universal. But they were standing there watching me. Then I was afraid: a woman so far removed from nature that the checkout clerk had to tell me which way the wind was blowing. And she heard it from someone in the coffee room. Then the men left, and I pushed the cart back. I live by trying to be what I'm doing. I could do nearly everything I do without thinking about it. But I'd be different."

His face was tender in the light of the fire; he said: "Yes."

"They collided with me: all this harmony I work for; this life of the spirit with the flesh. They walked into the kitchen and I said *No, God; not like this*, and I beat them with a skillet. But I'm not sure that was the answer to my prayer."

"It was."

"I don't know."

"What else could you have done?"

"I can't think of anything else. I know what I couldn't do. I couldn't turn the other cheek."

"Listen," he said, and he leaned closer and placed both palms on her cheeks. "You did what you had to do. It's a jungle out there."

"No. It's not out there. Everything is out there, and everything is in here." She touched her heart. "Hitting them, seeing their blood, seeing them fall. All afternoon I was amazed at my body. But that was me hitting them."

He lowered his hands, rested one on her shoulder, and said: "You *had* to. For yourself. For the children. For me."

"I don't even know what they wanted."

"You saw it in their eyes."

"I know what I wanted. And, no, I don't think I have the right to give away my life. Because of you and the children. I think the one in red wanted to rape me. Maybe that was all. Then the other one probably would have, too."

"*All?* LuAnn, that's reason enough to beat them till..." He paused, looking at her eyes. She could see him imagining himself attacking the two men. She said: "Till they were dead? On the kitchen floor? I don't know how close I came to killing them. Who knows, when you hit someone's face and head with a steel skillet? I'd do it again. But I have to know this, and remember this, and tell it to the children: I didn't hit those men so I could be alive for the children, or for you. I hit them so my blood would stay in my body; so I could keep breathing. And if it's that easy, how are we supposed to live? If evil can walk through the door, and there's a place deep in our hearts that knows how to look at its face, and beat it till it's broken and bleeding, till it crawls away. And we do this with rapture."

He moved closer to her. Their legs touched, their hips, their arms; and they sat looking at the fire.

DANCING AFTER HOURS

ANDRE DUBUS

For M.L.

Emily Moore was a forty-year-old bartender in a town in Massachusetts. On a July evening, after making three margaritas and giving them to Kay to take to a table, and drawing four mugs of beer for two young couples at the bar, wearing bathing suits and sweatshirts and smelling of sunscreen, she went outside to see the sun before it set. She blinked and stood on the landing of the wooden ramp that angled down the front wall of the bar. She smelled hot asphalt; when the wind blew from the east, she could smell the ocean here, and at her apartment, and sometimes she smelled it in the rain, but now the air was still. In front of the bar was a road, and across it were white houses and beyond them was a hill with green trees. A few cars passed. She looked to her right, at a grassy hill where the road curved; above the hill, the sun was low and the sky was red.

Emily wore a dark blue shirt with short sleeves and a pale yellow skirt; she had brown hair, and for over thirty years she had wanted a pretty face. For too long, as a girl and adolescent, then a young woman, she had believed her face was homely. Now she knew it was simply not pretty. Its parts were: her eyes, her nose, her mouth, her cheeks and jaw, and chin and brow; but, combined, they lacked the mysterious proportion of a pretty face during Emily's womanhood in America. Often, looking at photographs of models and actresses, she thought how disfiguring an eighth of an inch could be, if a beautiful woman's nose were moved laterally that distance, or an eye moved vertically. Her body had vigor, and beneath its skin were firm muscles, and for decades her female friends had told Emily they envied it. They admired her hair, too: it was thick and soft and fell in waves to her shoulders.

Believing she was homely as a girl and a young woman had deeply wounded her. She knew this affected her when she was with people, and she knew she could do nothing but feel it. She could not change. She also liked her face, even loved it; she had to: it held her eyes and nose and mouth and ears; they let her see and hear and smell and taste the world; and behind her face was her brain. Alone in her apartment, looking in the mirror above her dressing table, she saw her entire life, perhaps her entire self, in her face, and she could see it as it was when she was a child, a girl, a young woman. She knew now that most people's faces were plain, that most women of forty, even if they had been lovely once, were plain. But she felt that her face was an injustice she had suffered, and no matter how hard she tried, she could not achieve some new clarity, could not see herself as an ordinary and attractive woman walking the earth within meeting radius of hundreds of men whose eyes she could draw, whose hearts she could inspire.

On the landing outside the bar, she was gazing at the trees and blue sky and setting sun, and smelling the exhaust of passing cars. A red van heading east, with a black man driving and a white man beside him, turned left from the road and came into the parking lot. Then she saw that the white man sat in a wheelchair. Emily had worked here for over seven years, had never had a customer in a wheelchair, and had never wondered why the front entrance had a ramp instead of steps. The driver parked in a row of cars facing the bar, with an open space of twenty feet or so between the van and the ramp; he reached across the man in the wheelchair and closed the window and locked the door, then got out and walked around to the passenger side. The man in the wheelchair looked to his right at Emily and smiled; then, still looking at her, he moved smoothly backward till he was at the door behind the front seat, and turned his chair to face the window. Emily returned the smile. The black man turned a key at the side of the van, there was the low sound of a motor, and the door swung open. On a lift, the man in the wheelchair came out and, smiling at her again, descended to the ground. The wheelchair had a motor, and the man moved forward onto the asphalt, and the black man turned the key, and the lift rose and went into the van and the door closed.

Emily hoped the man's injury was not to his brain as well; she had a long shift ahead of her, until one o'clock closing, and she did not want the embarrassment of trying to speak to someone and listen to someone whose body was anchored in a chair and whose mind was afloat. She did not want to feel this way, but she knew she had no talent for it, and she would end by talking to him as though he were an infant, or a dog. He moved across the parking lot, toward the ramp and Emily. She turned to her right, so she faced him, and the sun.

The black man walked behind him but did not touch the chair. He wore jeans and a red T-shirt, he was tall and could still be in his twenties, and he exercised: she guessed with medium weights and running. The man in the moving chair wore a pale blue shirt with the cuffs rolled up twice at his wrists, tan slacks, and polished brown loafers. Emily glanced at his hands, their palms up and fingers curled and motionless on the armrests of his chair; he could work the chair's controls on the right armrest, but she knew he had not polished the loafers; knew he had not put them on his feet either, and had not put on his socks, or his pants and shirt. His clothes fit him loosely and his body looked small; *arrested,* she thought, and this made his head seem large, though it was not. She wanted to treat him well. She guessed he was in his mid-thirties, but all she saw clearly in his face was his condition: he was not new to it. His hair was brown, thinning on top, and at the sides it was combed back and trimmed. Someone took very good care of this man, and she looked beyond him at the black man's eyes. Then she pulled open the door, heard the couples in bathing suits and the couples at tables and the men at the dartboard; smells of cigarette smoke and beer and liquor came from the air-conditioned dark; she liked those smells. The man in the chair was climbing the ramp, and he said: "Thank you."

His voice was normal, and so was the cheerful light in his eyes, and she was relieved. She said: "I make the drinks, too."

"This gets better."

He smiled, and the black man said: "Our kind of place, Drew. The bartender waits outside, looking for us."

Drew was up the ramp, his feet close to Emily's legs; she stepped inside, her out-stretched left arm holding the door open; the black man reached over Drew and held the door and said: "I've got it."

She lowered her arm and turned to the dark and looked at Rita, who was watching from a swivel chair at the bar. Rita Bick was thirty-seven years old, and had red hair in a ponytail, and wore a purple shirt and a black skirt; she had tended bar since late morning, grilled and fried lunches, served the happy hour customers, and now was drinking a straight-up Manhattan she had made when Emily came to work. Her boyfriend had moved out a month ago, and she was smoking again. When Emily had left the bar to see the evening sun, she had touched Rita's shoulder in passing, then stopped when Rita said quietly: "What's so great about living a long time? Remote controls?" Emily had said: "What?" and Rita had said: "To change channels. While you lie in bed alone." Emily did not have a television in her bedroom, so she would not lie in bed with a remote control, watching movies and parts of movies till near dawn, when she could finally sleep. Now Rita stood and put her cigarette between her lips and pushed a table and four chairs out of Drew's path, then another table and its chairs, and at the next table she pulled away two chairs, and Drew rolled past Emily, the black man following, the door swinging shut on the sunlight. Emily watched Drew moving to the place Rita had made. Rita took the cigarette from her lips and looked at Drew.

"Will this be all right?"

"Absolutely. I like the way you make a road."

He turned his chair to the table and stopped, his back to the room, his face to the bar. Rita looked at Emily and said: "She'll do the rest. I'm off."

"Then join us. You left two chairs."

Emily was looking at the well-shaped back of the black man when he said: "Perfect math."

"Sure," Rita said, and went to the bar for her purse and drink. Emily stepped toward the table to take their orders, but Kay was coming from the men at the dartboard with a tray of glasses and beer bottles, and she veered to the table. Emily went behind the bar, a rectangle with a wall at one end and a swinging door to the kitchen. When Jeff had taught her the work, he had said: When you're behind the bar, you're the ship's captain; never leave the bar, and never let a customer behind it; keep their respect. She did. She was friendly with her customers; she wanted them to feel they were welcome here, and were missed if they did not come in often. She remembered the names of the regulars, their jobs and something about their families, and what they liked to drink. She talked with them when they wanted her to, and this was the hardest work of all; and standing for hours was hard, and she wore runner's shoes, and still her soles ached. She did not allow discourtesy or drunkenness.

The long sides of the bar were parallel to the building's front and rear, and the couples in bathing suits faced the entrance and, still talking, glanced to their right at Drew. Emily saw Drew notice them; he winked at her, and she smiled. He held a cigarette between his curled fingers. Kay was talking to him and the black man, holding her tray with one arm. Emily put a Bill Evans cassette in the player near the cash register, then stepped to the front of the bar and watched Kay in profile: the left side of her face, her short black hair, and her small body in a blue denim skirt and a black silk shirt. She was thirty and acted in the local theater and performed on nights when Emily was working, and she was always cheerful at the bar. Emily never saw her outside the bar, or Rita, either; she could imagine Rita at home because Rita told her about it; she could only imagine about Kay that she must sometimes be angry, or sad, or languid. Kay turned from the table and came six paces to the bar and put her tray on it; her eyelids were shaded, her lipstick pale. Emily's concentration when she was working was very good: the beach couples were talking and she could hear each word and Evans playing the piano and, at the same time, looking at Kay, she heard only her, as someone focusing on one singer in a chorus hears only her, and the other singers as well.

"Two margaritas, straight up, one in a regular glass because he has trouble with stems. A Manhattan for Rita. She says it's her last."

Dark-skinned, black-haired Kay Younger had gray-blue eyes, and she flirted subtly and seriously with Rita, evening after evening when Rita sat at the bar for two drinks after work. Rita smiled at Kay's flirting, and Emily did not believe she saw what Emily did: that Kay was falling in love. Emily hoped Kay would stop the fall, or direct its arc toward a woman who did not work at the bar. Emily wished she were not so cautious, or disillusioned; she longed for love but was able to keep her longing muted till late at night when she lay reading in bed, and it was trumpets, drums, French horns; and when she woke at noon, its sound in her soul was a distant fast train. Love did not bring happiness, it did not last, and it ended in pain. She did not want to believe this, and she was not certain that she did; perhaps she feared it was true in her own life, and her fear had become a feeling that tasted like disbelief. She did not want to see Rita and Kay in pain, and she did not want to walk into their pain when five nights a week she came to work. Love also pulled you downhill; then you had to climb again to the top, where you felt solidly alone with your integrity and were able to enjoy work again, and food and exercise and friends. Kay lit a cigarette and rested it on an ashtray, and Emily picked it up and drew on it and put it back; she blew smoke into the ice chest and reached for the tequila in the speed rack.

* * * * *

The beach couples and dart throwers were gone, someone sat on every chair at the bar, and at twelve of the fifteen tables, and Jeff was in his place. He was the manager, and he sat on the last chair at the back of the bar, before its gate. A Chet Baker cassette was playing, and Emily was working fast and smoothly, making drinks, washing glasses, talking to customers who spoke to her, punching tabs on the cash register, putting money in it, giving change, and stuffing bills and dropping coins into the brandy snifter that held her tips. Rita took her empty glass to Emily; it had been her second Manhattan and she had sipped it, had sat with Drew and the black man while they drank three margaritas. There were no windows in the bar, and Emily imagined the quiet dusk outside and Rita in her purple shirt walking into it. She said: "Jeff could cook you a steak."

"That's sweet. I have fish at home. And a potato. And salad."

"It's good that you're cooking."

"Do you? At night."

"It took me years."

"Amazing."

"What?"

"How much will it takes. I watch TV while I eat. But I cook. If I stay and drink with these guys, it could be something I'd start doing. Night shifts are better."

"I can't sleep anyway."

"I didn't know that. You mean all the time?"

"Every night, since college."

"Can you take a pill?"

"I read. Around four I sleep."

"I'd go crazy. See you tomorrow."

"Take care."

Rita turned and waved at Drew and the black man and walked to the door, looking at no one, and went outside. Emily imagined her walking into her apartment, listening to her telephone messages, standing at the machine, her heart beating with hope and dread; then putting a potato in the oven, taking off her shoes, turning on the television, to bring light and sound, faces and bodies into the room.

Emily had discipline: every night she read two or three poems twice, then a novel or stories till she slept. Eight hours later she woke and ate grapefruit or a melon, and cereal with a banana or berries and skimmed milk, and wheat toast with nothing on it. An hour after eating, she left her apartment and walked five miles in fifty-three minutes; the first half mile was in her neighborhood, and the next two were on a road through woods and past a farm with a meadow where cows stood. In late afternoon she cooked fish or chicken, and rice, a yellow vegetable and a green one. On the days when she did not have to work, she washed her clothes and cleaned her apartment, bought food, and went to a video store to rent a movie, or in a theater that night watched one with women friends. All of this sustained her body and soul, but they also isolated her: she became what she could see and hear, smell and taste and touch; like and dislike; think about and talk about; and they became the world. Then, in her long nights, when it seemed everyone on earth was asleep while she lay reading in bed, sorrow was tangible in the dark hall to her bedroom door, and in the dark rooms she could not see from her bed. It was there, in the lamplight, that she knew she would never bear and love children; that tomorrow would require of her the same strength and rituals of today; that if she did not nourish herself with food, gain a balancing peace of soul with a long walk, and immerse herself in work, she could not keep sorrow at bay, and it would consume her. In the lamplight she read, and she was opened to the world by imagined women and men and children, on pages she held in her hands, and the sorrow in the darkness remained, but she was consoled, as she became one with the earth and its creatures: its dead, its living, its living after her own death; one with the sky and water, and with a single leaf falling from a tree.

A man at the bar pushed his empty glass and beer bottle toward Emily, and she opened a bottle and brought it with a glass. Kay was at her station with a tray of glasses, and said: "Rita left."

"Being brave."

Emily took a glass from the tray and emptied it in one of two cylinders in front of her; a strainer at its top caught the ice and fruit; in the second cylinder she dipped the glass in water, then placed it in the rack of the small dishwasher. She looked at each glass she rinsed and at all three sides of the bar as she listened to Kay's order. Then she made piña coladas in the blender, whose noise rose above the music and the voices at the bar, and she made gin and tonics, smelling the wedges of lime she squeezed; and made two red sea breezes. Kay left with the drinks and Emily stood facing the tables, where the room was darker, and listened to Baker's trumpet. She tapped her fingers in rhythm on the bar. Behind her was Jeff, and she felt him watching her.

Jefferson Gately was a tall and broad man who had lost every hair on top of his head; he had brown hair on the sides and back, and let it grow over his collar. He had a thick brown mustache with gray in it. Last fall, when the second of his two daughters started college, his wife told him she wanted a divorce. He was shocked. He was an intelligent and watchful man, and at work he was gentle, and Emily could not imagine him living twenty-three years with a woman and not knowing precisely when she no longer wanted him in her life. He told all of this to Emily on autumn nights, with a drink after the bar closed, and she believed he did not know his wife's heart, but she did not understand why. He lived alone in a small apartment, and his brown eyes were often pensive. At night he sat on his chair and watched the crowd and drank club soda with bitters; when people wanted food, he cooked hamburgers or steaks on the grill, potatoes and clams or fish in the fryers, and made sandwiches and salads. The bar's owner was old and lived in Florida and had no children, and Jeff would inherit the bar. Twice a year he flew to Florida to eat dinner with the old man, who gave Jeff all his trust and small yearly pay raises.

In spring Jeff had begun talking differently to Emily, when she was not making drinks, when she went to him at the back of the bar. He still talked only about his daughters and the bar, or wanting to buy a boat to ride in on the river, to fish from on the sea; but he sounded as if he were confiding in her; and his eyes were giving her something: they seemed poised to reveal a depth she could enter if she chose. One night in June he asked Emily if she would like to get together sometime, maybe for lunch. The muscles in her back and chest and legs and arms tightened, and she said: "Why not," and saw in his face that her eyes and voice had told him no and that she had hurt him.

She had hurt herself, too, and she could not say this to Jeff: she wanted to have lunch with him. She liked him, and lunch was in daylight and not dangerous; you met at the restaurant and talked and ate, then went home, or shopping for groceries or beach sandals. She wanted to have drinks and dinner with him, too, but dinner was timeless; there could be coffee and brandy, and it was night and you parted to sleep; a Friday dinner could end Saturday morning, in a shower that soothed your skin but not your heart, which had opened you to pain. Now there was AIDS, and she did not want to risk death for something that was already a risk, something her soul was too tired to grapple with again. She did not keep condoms in her apartment because two winters ago, after one night with a thin, pink-faced, sweet-eyed man who never called her again, she decided that next time she made love she would know about it long before it happened, and she did not need to be prepared for sudden passion. She put her box of condoms in a grocery bag and then in a garbage bag, and on a cold night after work she put the bag on the sidewalk in front of her apartment. In a drawer, underneath her stacked underwear, she had a vibrator. On days when most of her underwear was in the laundry basket, the vibrator moved when she opened and closed the drawer, and the sound of fluted plastic rolling on wood made her feel caught by someone who watched, someone who was above this. She loved what the vibrator did, and was able to forget it was there until she wanted it, but once in a while she felt shame, thinking of dying, and her sister or brother or parents finding the vibrator. Sometimes after using it, she wept.

* * * * *

It was ten-fifteen by the bar clock that Jeff kept twenty minutes fast. Tonight he wore a dark brown shirt with short sleeves, and white slacks; his arms and face and the top of his head were brown, with a red hue from the sun, and he looked clean and confident. It was a weekday, and in the afternoon he had fished from a party boat. He had told Emily in winter that his rent for a bedroom, a living room, a kitchen, and bathroom was six hundred dollars a month; his car was old; and until his wife paid him half the value of the house she had told him to leave, he could not buy a boat. He paid fifteen dollars to go on the party boat and fish for half a day, and when he did this, he was visibly happier. Now Emily looked at him, saw his glass with only ice in it, and brought him a club soda with a few drops of bitters; the drink was the color of Kay's lipstick. He said: "I'm going to put wider doors on the bathroom." Their faces were close over the bar, so the woman sitting to the right of Jeff could not hear unless she eavesdropped. "That guy can't get in."

"I think he has a catheter. His friend took something to the bathroom."

"I know. But the next one in a chair may want to use a toilet. He likes Kay. He can feel everything, but only in his brain and heart."

She had seen Drew talking to Kay and smiling at her, and now she realized that she had seen him as a man living outside of passion. She looked at Jeff's eyes, feeling that her soul had atrophied; that it had happened without her notice. Jeff said: "What?"

"I should have known."

"No. I had a friend like him. He always looked happy and I knew he was never happy. A mine got him, in Vietnam."

"Were you there?"

"Not with him. I knew him before and after."

"But you were there."

"Yes."

She saw herself facedown in a foxhole while the earth exploded as close to her as the walls of the bar. She said: "I couldn't do that."

"Neither could I."

"Now, you mean."

"Now, or then."

"But you did."

"I was lucky. We used to take my friend fishing. His chair weighed two hundred and fifty pounds. We carried him up the steps and lifted him over the side. We'd bait for him, and he'd fold his arms around the rod. When he got a bite, we'd reel it in. Mike looked happy on a boat. But he got very tired."

"Where is he now?"

"He died."

"Is he the reason we have a ramp?"

"Yes. But he died before I worked here. One winter pneumonia killed him. I just never got to the bathroom doors."

"You got a lot of sun today."

"Bluefish, too."

"Really?"

"You like them?"

"On the grill. With mayonnaise and lemon."

"In foil. I have a grill on my deck. It's not really a deck. It's a landing outside the kitchen, on the second floor. The size of a closet."

"There's Kay. I hope you had sunscreen."

He smiled and shook his head, and she went to Kay, thinking they were like that: they drank too much; they got themselves injured; they let the sun burn their skin; they went to war. The cautious ones bored her. Kay put down her tray of glasses and slid two filled ashtrays to Emily, who emptied them in the garbage can. Kay wiped them with a paper napkin and said: "Alvin and Drew want steak and fries. No salads. Margaritas now, and Tecates with the meal."

"Alvin."

"Personal care attendant. His job."

"They look like friends."

"They are."

Emily looked at Jeff, but he had heard and was standing; he stepped inside the bar and went through the swinging door to the kitchen. Emily rubbed lime on the rims of glasses and pushed them into the container of thick salt, scooped ice into the blender and poured tequila, and imagined Alvin cutting Drew's steak, sticking the fork into a piece, maybe feeding it to him; and that is when she knew that Alvin wiped Drew's shit. Probably as Drew lay on his bed, Alvin lifted him and slid a bedpan under him; then he would have to roll him on one side to wipe him clean, and take the bedpan to the toilet. Her body did not shudder, but she felt as if it shuddered; she knew her face was composed, but it seemed to grimace. She heard Roland Kirk playing tenor saxophone on her cassette, and words at the bar, and voices from the tables; she breathed the smells of tequila and cigarette smoke, gave Kay the drinks, then looked at Alvin. Kay went to the table and bent forward to place the drinks. Drew spoke to her. Alvin bathed him somehow, too, kept his flesh clean for his morale and health. She looked at Alvin for too long; he turned and looked at her. She looked away, at the front door.

* * * * *

It was not the shit. Shit was nothing. It was the spiritual pain that twisted her soul: Drew's helplessness, and Alvin reaching into it with his hands. She had stopped teaching because of pain: she had gone with passion to high school students, year after year, and always there was one student, or even five, who wanted to feel a poem or story or novel, and see more clearly because of it. But Emily's passion dissolved in the other students. They were young and robust, and although she knew their apathy was above all a sign of their being confined by classrooms and adolescence, it still felt like apathy. It made Emily feel isolated and futile, and she thought that if she were a gym teacher or a teacher of dance, she could connect with her students. The women and men who coached athletic teams or taught physical education or dance seemed always to be in harmony with themselves and their students. In her last three years she realized she was becoming scornful and bitter, and she worked to control the tone of her voice, and what she said to students, and what she wrote on their papers. She taught without confidence or hope, and felt like a woman standing at a road-side, reading poems aloud into the wind as cars filled with teenagers went speeding by. She was tending bar in summer and finally she asked Jeff if she could work all year. She liked the work, she stopped taking sleeping pills because when she slept no longer mattered, and, with her tips, she earned more money. She did not want to teach again, or work with teenagers, or have to talk to anyone about the books she read. But she knew that pain had defeated her, while other teachers had endured it, or had not felt it as sharply.

Because of pain, she had turned away from Jeff, a man whom she looked forward to seeing at work. She was not afraid of pain; she was tired of it; and sometimes she thought being tired of it was worse than fear, that losing fear meant she had lost hope as well. If this were true, she would not be able to love with her whole heart, for she would not have a whole heart; and only a man who had also lost hope, and who would settle for the crumbs of the feast, would return her love with the crumbs of his soul. For a long time she had not trusted what she felt for a man, and for an even longer time, beginning in high school, she had deeply mistrusted what men felt for her, or believed they felt, or told her they felt. She chronically believed that, for a man, love was a complicated pursuit of an orgasm, and its evanescence was directly proportionate to the number of orgasms a particular man achieved, before his brain cleared and his heart cooled. She suspected this was also true of herself, though far less often than it was for a man.

When a man's love for Emily ended, she began to believe that he had never loved her; that she was a homely fool, a hole where the man had emptied himself. She would believe this until time healed the pain. Then she would know that in some way the man had loved her. She never believed her face was what first attracted these men; probably her body had, or something she said; but finally they did like her face; they looked at it, touched it with their hands, kissed it. She only knew now, as a forty-year-old woman who had never lived with a man, that she did not know the truth: if sexual organs were entities that drew people along with them, forcing them to collide and struggle, she wanted to be able to celebrate them; if the heart with intrepid fervor could love again and again, using the sexual organs in its dance, she wanted to be able to exalt its resilience. But nothing was clear, and she felt that if she had been born pretty, something would be clear, whether or not it were true.

She wanted equilibrium: she wanted to carry what she had to carry, and to walk with order and strength. She had never been helpless, and she thought of Drew: his throbless penis with a catheter in it, his shit. If he could not feel a woman, did he even know if he was shitting? She believed she could not bear such helplessness, and would prefer death. She thought: *I can walk. Feed myself. Shower. Shit in a toilet. Make love.* She was neither grateful nor relieved; she was afraid. She had never imagined herself being crippled, and now, standing behind the bar, she felt her spine as part of her that could be broken, the spinal cord severed; saw herself in a wheelchair with a motor, her body attenuating, her face seeming larger; saw a hired woman doing everything for her and to her.

* * * * *

Kay's lighter and cigarettes were on the bar; Emily lit one, drew on it twice, and placed it on the ashtray. Kay was coming out of the dark of the tables, into the dim light at the bar. She picked up the cigarette and said: "Oh, look. It came lit."

She ordered, and Emily worked with ice and limes and vodka and gin and grapefruit juice and salt, with club soda and quinine water, and scotch and bottles of beer and clean glasses, listening to Roland Kirk and remembering him twenty years ago in the small club on the highway, where she sat with two girlfriends. The place was dark, the tables so close to each other that the waitresses sidled, and everyone sat facing the bandstand and the blind black man wearing sunglasses. He had a rhythm section and a percussionist, and sometimes he played two saxophones at once. He grinned; he talked to the crowd, his head moving as if he were looking at them. He said: "It's nice, coming to work blind. Not seeing who's fat or skinny. Ugly. Or pretty. Know what I mean?"

Emily knew then, sitting between her friends, and knew now, working in this bar that was nearly as dark as the one where he had played; he was dead, but here he was, his music coming from the two speakers high on the walls, coming softly. Maybe she was the only person in the bar who heard him at this moment, as she poured gin; of course everyone could hear him, as people heard rain outside their walls. In the bar she never heard rain or cars, or saw snow or dark skies or sunlight. Maybe Jeff was listening to Kirk while he cooked. And only to be kind, to immerse herself in a few seconds of pure tenderness, she took two pilsner glasses from the shelf and opened the ice chest and pushed the glasses deep into the ice, for Alvin and Drew.

Kirk had walked the earth with people who only saw. So did Emily. But she saw who was fat or ugly, and if they were men, she saw them as if through an upstairs window. Twenty years ago, Kirk's percussionist stood beside him, playing a tambourine, and Kirk was improvising, playing fast, and Emily was drumming with her hands on the table. Kirk reached to the percussionist and touched his arm and stepped toward the edge of the bandstand. The percussionist stepped off it and held up his hand; Kirk took it and stepped down and followed the percussionist, followed the sound of the tambourine, playing the saxophone, his body swaying. People stood and pushed their tables and chairs aside, and, clapping and exclaiming, followed Kirk. Everyone was standing, and often Kirk reached out and held someone's waist, and hugged. In the dark they came toward Emily, who was standing with her friends. The percussionist's hand was fast on his tambourine; he was smiling; he was close; then he passed her, and Kirk was there. His left arm encircled her, his hand pressing her waist; she smelled his sweat as he embraced her so hard that she lost balance and stood on her toes; she could feel the sound of the saxophone in her body. He released her. People were shouting and clapping, and she stepped into the line, held the waist of a man in front of her; her two friends were behind her, one holding her waist. She was making sounds but not words, singing with Kirk's saxophone. They weaved around tables and chairs, then back to the bandstand, to the drummer and the bass and piano players, and the percussionist stepped up on it and turned to Kirk, and Kirk took his hand and stepped up and faced the clapping, shouting crowd. Then Kirk, bending back, blew one long high note, then lowered his head and played softly, slowly, some old and sweet melody. Emily's hands, raised and parted to clap, lowered to her sides. She walked backward to her table, watching Kirk. She and her friends quietly pulled their table and chairs into place and sat. Emily quietly sat, and waitresses moved in the dark, bent close to the mouths of people softly ordering drinks. The music was soothing, was loving, and Emily watched Kirk and felt that everything good was possible.

It would be something like that, she thought now, *something ineffable that comes from outside and fills us; something that changes the way we see what we see; something that allows us to see what we don't.*

* * * * *

She served four people at the bar, and Jeff came through the swinging door with two plates and forks and knives, and went through the gate and around the bar to Alvin and Drew. He stood talking to them; Alvin took the plate Jeff had put in front of Drew, and began cutting the steak. Jeff walked back to the bar, and Emily opened two bottles of Tecate and pulled the glasses out of the ice chest. Jeff said: "Nice, Emily."

Something lovely spread in her heart, blood warmed her cheeks, and tears were in her eyes; then they flowed down her face, stopped near her nose, and with the fingers of one hand she wiped them, and blinked and wiped her eyes, and they were clear. She glanced around the bar; no one had seen. Jeff said: "Are you all right?"

"I just had a beautiful memory of Roland Kirk."

"Lucky man." He held the bottle necks with one hand, and she put the glasses in his other hand; he held only their bottoms, to save the frost.

"I didn't know him. I saw him play once. That's him now."

"That's him? I was listening in the kitchen. The oil bubbled in time."

"My blood did, that night."

"So you cry at what's beautiful?"

"Sometimes. How about you?"

"It stays inside. I end up crying at silly movies."

He took the beer to Alvin and Drew, and stood talking; then he sat with them. A woman behind Emily at the bar called her name, and the front door opened and Rita in a peach shirt and jeans came in, and looked at Drew and Alvin and Jeff. Then she looked at Emily and smiled and came toward the bar. Emily smiled, then turned to the woman who had called; she sat with two other women. Emily said: "All around?"

"All around," the woman said.

Emily made daiquiris in the blender and brought them with both hands gripping the three stems, then went to Rita, who was standing between two men sitting at the bar. Rita said: "Home sucked." She gave Emily a five-dollar bill. "Dry vermouth on the rocks, with a twist."

Emily looked at Jeff and Alvin and Drew; they were watching and smiling. She poured Rita's drink and gave it to her and put her change on the bar, and said: "It's a glorious race."

"People?" Rita said, and pushed a dollar toward Emily. "Tell me about it."

"So much suffering, and we keep getting out of bed in the morning."

She saw the man beside Rita smiling. Emily said to him: "Don't we."

"For some reason."

"We get hungry," Rita said. "We have to pee."

She picked up the vermouth and went to Jeff and Alvin and Drew; Jeff stood and got a chair from another table. Alvin stuck Drew's fork into a piece of meat and placed the fork between Drew's fingers, and Drew raised it to his mouth. He could grip the French fries with his fingers, lift them from the plate. Kay went to their table and, holding her tray of glasses against her hip, leaned close to Rita and spoke, and Rita laughed. Kay walked smiling to the bar.

When Alvin and Drew finished eating, Drew held a cigarette and Rita gave him a light. Emily had seen him using his lighter while Rita was at home. He could not quite put out his cigarettes; he jabbed them at the ashtray and dropped them and they smoldered. Sometimes Alvin put them out, and sometimes he did not, and Emily thought about fire, where Drew lived, then wondered if he were ever alone. Jeff stood with their empty plates and went to the kitchen, and she thought of Drew, after this happened to him, learning each movement he could perform alone, and each one he could not; learning what someone else had to help him do, and what someone else had to do for him. He would have learned what different people did not like to do. Alvin did not smoke, or he had not tonight. Maybe he disliked touching cigarettes and disliked smelling them burning to the filter in an ashtray, so sometimes he put them out and sometimes smelled them. But he could empty bags of piss, and wipe shit. Probably he inserted the catheter.

Two summers ago a young woman came to work as a bartender, to learn the job while doing it. Jeff worked with her, and on her first three days the noon crowd wanted fried clams, and she told Jeff she could not stand clams but she would do it. She picked them up raw and put them in batter and fried them, and they nauseated her. She did not vomit, but she looked all through lunch as if she would. On the fourth day, Jeff cooked, but when she smelled the frying clams while she was making drinks, she could see them raw and feel them in her hands and smell them, and she was sick as she worked and talked with customers. She had learned the essential drinks in four days and most of the rare ones, and Jeff called a friend who managed a bar whose only food was peanuts, to make the customers thirsty, and got her a job.

So, was anyone boundless? Most of the time, you could avoid what disgusted you. But if you always needed someone to help you simply live, and that person was disgusted by your cigarettes, or your body, or what came out of it, you would sense that disgust, be infected by it, and become disgusted by yourself. Emily did not mind the smell of her own shit, the sight of it on toilet paper and in the water. There was only a stench if someone else smelled it, only disgust if someone else saw it. Drew's body had knocked down the walls and door of his bathroom; living without this privacy, he also had to rely on someone who did not need him to be private. It was an intimacy babies had, and people like Drew, and the ill and dying. And who could go calmly and tenderly and stoutly into his life? For years she had heard married women speak with repugnance of their husbands: their breath, their farts, their fat stomachs and asses, their lust, their golf, their humor, their passions, their loves. Maybe Jeff's wife was one of these; maybe she had been with him too long; maybe he took home too many fish.

Kirk had said: "Know what I mean?" To love without the limits of seeing; so to love without the limits of the flesh. As Kirk danced through the crowd, he had hugged women and men, not knowing till his hand and arm touched their flesh. When he hugged Emily, she had not felt like a woman in the embrace of a man; she melded; she was music.

Alvin stood and came to the bar and leaned toward her and said: "Are we close to a motel?"

"Sure. Where did you come from?"

"Boston."

"Short trip."

"First leg of one. He likes to get out and look around." He smiled. "We stopped for a beer."

"I'm glad you did. You can use the bar phone."

She picked up the telephone and the book beside the cash register and put them on the bar. She opened the Yellow Pages. Alvin said: "We need the newest one."

"Are the old ones bad?"

"Eye of a needle."

"Are you with him all the time?"

"Five days a week. Another guy takes five nights. Another the weekend, day and night. I travel with him."

"Have you always done this work?"

"No. I fell into it."

"How?"

"I wanted to do grand things. I read his ad, and called him."

"What grand things?"

"For the world. It was an abstraction."

* * * * *

Now the bar was closed and they had drawn two tables together; Emily was drinking vodka and tonic, Louis Armstrong was playing, and she listened to his trumpet, and to Drew; he was looking at her, his face passionate, joyful.

"You could do it," he said. "It's up in Maine. They teach you for—what?" He looked at Alvin. "An hour?"

"At most."

Kay said to Alvin: "Did you do it?"

"No. I don't believe in jumping out of airplanes. I don't feel good about staying inside of one, either."

"Neither do I," Emily said.

"You could do it," Drew said, watching Emily. He was drinking beer, but slowly, and he did not seem drunk. Alvin had been drinking club soda since they ate dinner. "You could come with me. They talk to you; then they take you up." Emily saw Drew being carried by Alvin and other men into a small airplane, lowered into a seat, and strapped to it. "They told me there was a ground wind. They said if I was a normal, the wind wouldn't be a problem. But—"

Jeff said: "They said 'a normal'?"

"No. What the guy said was: 'With your condition you've got a ninety percent chance of getting hurt.' Drew smiled. "I told him I've lived with nine-to-one odds for a long time. So we went up in their little plane." Emily could not imagine being paralyzed, but she felt enclosed in a small plane; from inside the plane she saw it take off. "The guy was strong, very confident. Up in the air he lifted me out of the seat and strapped me to him. My back to his chest. We went to the door of the plane, and I looked at the blue sky."

"Weren't you terrified?" Emily lit one of Drew's cigarettes and placed it between his fingers. When she had cleaned the bar and joined them at the table, she had told him and Alvin her name. Drew Purdy. Alvin Parker. She shook their hands, Alvin rising from his chair; when Drew moved his hand upward, she had inserted hers between his fingers and his palm. His hand was soft.

"It felt like fear," Drew said. "But it was adrenaline. I didn't have any bad pictures in my head: like the chute not opening. Leaving a mess on the ground for Alvin to pray over. Then he jumped; we jumped. And I had this rush, like nothing I had ever felt. Better than anything I ever felt. And I used to do a lot, before I got hurt. But this was another world, another body. We were free-falling. Dropping down from the sky like a hawk, and everything was beautiful, green and blue. Then he opened the chute. And you know what? It was absolutely quiet up there. I was looking down at the people on the ground. They were small, and I could hear their voices. I thought I heard Alvin. Probably I imagined that. I couldn't hear words, but I could hear men and women and children. All those voices up in the sky."

Emily could see it, hear it, and her arms and breast wanted to hug him because he had done this; her hand touched his, rested on his fingers; then she took his cigarette and drew on it and put it between his fingers and blew smoke over his head.

Kay said: "I think I'd like the parachute. But I couldn't jump out of the plane."

Drew smiled. "Neither could I."

"I don't like underwater," Rita said. "And I don't like in the air."

"Tell them what happened," Alvin said.

"He didn't think I should do it."

"I thought you should do it on a different day, after what he told you. I thought you could wait."

"You knew I couldn't wait."

"Yes." Alvin looked at Emily. "It's true. He couldn't."

"I broke both my legs."

"*No*," Emily said.

Jeff said: "Did you feel them?"

Rita was shaking her head; Kay was watching Drew.

"No," Drew said. "They made a video of it. You can hear my legs break. The wind dragged us, and I couldn't do anything with my legs."

"He was laughing the whole time," Alvin said. "While the chute was pulling them on the ground. He's on top of the guy, and he's laughing and shouting: 'This is great, this is great.' And on the video you can hear his bones snapping."

"When did you know?" Jeff said.

"On the third day. When my feet were swollen, and Alvin couldn't get my shoes on."

"You never felt pain?" Rita said.

"Not like you do. It was like a pinball machine, this little ball moving around. So in the hospital they sent me a shrink. To see if I had a death wish. If a normal sky dives and breaks some bones, they don't ask him if he wanted to die. They ask quads. I told him if I wanted to die, I wouldn't have paid a guy with a parachute. I told him it was better than sex. I told him he should try it."

"What did he say?" Jeff said.

"He said he didn't think I had a death wish."

Rita said: "How did you get hurt?"

"Diving into a wave."

"Oh my God," Emily said. "I love diving into waves."

"Don't stop." He smiled. "You could slip in the shower. I know a guy like me, who fell off his bed. He wasn't drunk; he was asleep. He doesn't know how he fell. He woke up on the floor, a quad."

* * * * *

She was sipping her third drink and smoking one of Rita's cigarettes, and looking over Jeff's head at the wall and ceiling, listening to Paul Desmond playing saxophone with Brubeck. Rita's face was turned to Kay, and Emily could only hear their voices; Jeff and Alvin and Drew were planning to fish. She looked at them and said: "Paul Desmond—the guy playing sax—once lost a woman he loved to an older and wealthy man. One night he was sitting in a restaurant, and they came in, the young woman and the man. Desmond watched them going to their table and said: 'So this is how the world ends, not with a whim but a banker.'"

Rita and Kay were looking at her.

"I like that," Drew said.

"He was playing with a T.S. Eliot line. The poet. Who said 'April is the cruelest month.' That's why they called him T.S."

They were smiling at her. Jeff's eyes were bright.

"I used to talk this way. Five days a week."

"What were you?" Drew said.

"A teacher."

She was looking at Drew and seeing him younger, with strong arms and legs, in a bathing suit, running barefoot across hot sand to the water, his feet for the last time holding his weight on the earth, his legs moving as if they always would, his arms swinging at his sides; then he was in the surf, running still, but very slowly in the water; the cold water thrilled him, cleared his mind; he moved toward the high waves; he was grinning. Waves broke in front of him and rushed against his waist, his thighs, his penis. A rising wave crested and he dived into it as it broke, and it slapped his legs and back and turned him, turned him just so, and pushed him against the bottom.

Alvin asked Rita to dance, and Kay asked Jeff. They pushed tables and chairs and made a space on the floor, and held each other, moving to Desmond's slow song. Emily said: "When this happened to you, who pulled you out of the water?"

"Two buddies. They rode in on the wave that got me. They looked around and saw me. I was like a big rag doll in the water. I'd go under, I'd come up. Mostly under."

"Did you know how bad it was?"

"I was drowning. That's what I was afraid of till they came and got me. Then I was scared because I couldn't move. They put me on the beach, and then I felt the pain; and I couldn't move my legs and arms. I was twenty-one years old, and I knew."

Last night Emily had not worked and yesterday afternoon she had gone to the beach with a book of stories by Edna O'Brien. She rubbed sunscreen on her body and lay on a towel and read five stories. When she finished a story, she ran in the surf, and dived into a wave, opened her eyes to the salt water, stood and shook her hair and faced the beach, looking over her shoulder at the next wave coming in, then dived with it as it broke, and it pushed and pulled her to the beach, until her outstretched hands and then her face and breasts were on sand, and the surf washed over her.

* * * * *

John Coltrane was playing a ballad, and Jeff looked at her and said: "Would you like to dance?"

She nodded and stood, walked around tables, and in the open space turned to face him. Rita and Alvin came and started to dance. Emily took Jeff's hand and held him behind his waist, and they danced to the saxophone, her breasts touching his chest; he smelled of scotch and smoke; his moustache was soft on her brow. She looked to her left at Drew: he had turned the chair around, and was watching. Now Kay rose from her chair and stood in front of him; she bent forward, held his hands, and began to dance. She swayed to the saxophone's melody, and her feet moved in rhythm, forward, back, to her sides. Emily could not see Drew's face. She said: "I don't know if Kay should be doing that."

"He jumped from an airplane."

"But he could feel it. The thrill anyway. The air on his face."

"He can feel Kay, too. She's there. She's dancing with him." He led Emily in graceful turns toward the front wall, so she could see Drew's face. "Look. He's happy."

Drew was smiling; his head was dancing: down, up to his right, down, up to his left. Emily looked at Jeff's eyes and said: "You told me your friend always looked happy and you knew he was never happy."

"It's complicated. I knew he couldn't *enjoy* being a quad. I knew he missed his body: fishing, hunting, swimming, dancing, girls, just *walk*ing. He probably even missed being a soldier, when he was scared and tired, and wet and hot and thirsty and bug-bit; but he was whole and strong. So I say he was never happy; he only looked happy. But he had friends, and he had fun. It took a lot of will for him to have fun. He had to do it in spite of everything. Not because of everything."

He turned her and dipped—she was leaning backward and only his arms kept her balanced; he pulled her up and held her close.

"On a fishing boat I lose myself. I don't worry about things. I just look at the ocean and feel the sun. It's the ocean. The ocean takes me there. Mike had to do it himself. He couldn't just step onto a boat and let the ocean take him. First he had to be carried on. Anybody who's helpless is afraid; you could see it in his eyes, while he joked with us. I'm sure he was sad, too, while we carried him. He was a soldier, Emily. That's not something he could forget. Then out on the ocean, he couldn't really hold the rod and fish. And his body was always pulling on him. He had spasms on the boat, and fatigue."

Coltrane softly blew a low note and held it, the drummer tapping cymbals, and the cassette ended. Emily withdrew her hand from Jeff's back, but he still held hers, and her right hand. He said: "He told me once: 'I wake up tired.' His body was his enemy, and when he fought it, he lost. What he had to do was ignore it. That was the will. That was how he was happy."

"Ignore it?"

"Move beyond it."

He released her back and lowered her hand, and shifted his grip on it and held it as they walked toward the table; then Jeff stopped her. He said: "He had something else. He was grateful."

"For what?"

"That he wasn't blown to pieces. And that he still had his brain."

They walked and at the table he let go of her hand and she stood in front of Drew, and said: "You looked good."

Kay sat beside Rita; Jeff and Alvin stood talking.

"My wife and I danced like that."

"Your wife? You said—" Then she stopped; a woman had loved him, had married him after the wave crippled him. She glanced past him; no one had heard.

"Right," he said. "I met her when I was like this."

"Shit."

He nodded. She said: "Would you like a beer?"

"Yes."

She walked past the table, then stopped and looked back. Drew was turning his chair around, looking at her now, and he said: "Do you have Old Blue Eyes?"

"Not him," Rita said.

"He's good to dance to," Kay said.

"I've got him," Emily said. "Anybody want drinks?"

She went behind the bar and made herself a vodka and tonic. Kay and Rita came to the bar, stood with their shoulders and arms touching, and Emily gave them a Tecate and a club soda, and they took them to Drew and Alvin. They came back and Emily put in the Sinatra cassette and poured vermouth for Rita and made a salty dog with tequila for Kay. While she was pouring the grapefruit juice, Kay said to Rita: "Can you jitterbug?"

"Girl, if you lead, I can follow."

Kay put her right hand on Rita's waist, held Rita's right hand with her left, then lifted their hands and turned Rita in a circle, letting Rita's hand turn in hers; then, facing each other, they danced. Kay sang with Sinatra:

Till the tune ends
We're dancing in the dark
And it soon ends

Emily sang:

We're waltzing in the wonder
Of why we're here
Time hurries by, we're here
And gone—

Emily watched her pretty friends dancing, and looked beyond them at Jeff and Alvin, tapping the table with their fingers, watching, grinning; Drew was singing. She smiled and sang and played drums on the bar till the song ended. Then she poured Jeff a scotch on ice and went to the table with it, and he stood and pulled out the chair beside him, and she sat in it.

She looked at Drew. She could not see pallor in the bar light, but she knew from his eyes that he was very tired. Or maybe it was not his eyes; maybe she saw his fatigue because she could see Jeff's friend, tired on the fishing boat, talking and laughing with Jeff, a fishing rod held in his arms. Rita and Kay sat across from her, beside Alvin. Emily leaned in front of Jeff and said to Drew: "How are you?"

"Fine."

Her right knee was touching Jeff's thigh, her right arm resting on his, and her elbow touched his chest. For a moment she did not notice this; then she did; she was touching him as easily as she had while dancing, and holding his hand coming back to the table. She said to Drew: "You can sleep late tomorrow."

"I will. Then we'll go to Maine."

"You're *jump*ing again?"

"Not this time. We're going to look at the coast. Then we'll come back here and fish with Jeff."

She looked at Jeff, so close that her hair had touched his face as she turned. She drew back, looking at his eyes, seeing him again carrying a two-hundred-and-fifty-pound wheelchair with a man in it up the steps to the wharf, and up the steps to the boat: Jeff and Alvin and someone else, as many men as the width of the steps would allow; then on the boat at sea, Jeff standing beside Drew, helping him fish. She said: "Really? When?"

"Monday," Jeff said.

She sat erectly again and drank and glanced at Kay and Rita in profile, talking softly, smiling, their hands on the table, holding cigarettes and drinks.

* * * * *

Sinatra was singing "Angel Eyes," and Kay and Rita were dancing slowly, and Jeff and Alvin were in the kitchen making ham and cheese sandwiches. Kay was leading, holding Rita's hand between their shoulders, her right hand low on Rita's back; they turned and Emily looked at Rita's face: her eyes were closed. Her hand was lightly moving up and down Kay's back, and Emily knew what Rita was feeling: a softening thrill in her heart, a softening peace in her muscles; and Kay, too. She looked at Drew.

"You danced with your wife, you—" She stopped.

"Are you asking how we made love?"

"No. Yes."

"I can have an erection. I don't feel it. But you know what people can do in bed, if they want to."

Looking at his eyes, she saw herself with the vibrator.

"I was really asking you what happened. I just didn't have the guts."

"I met her at a party. We got married; we had a house. For three years. One guy in a *hun*dred with my kind of injury can get his wife pregnant. Then, wow, she was. Then on New Year's Eve my wife and my ex-best friend came to the bedroom, and stood there looking down at me. I'd thought they spent a lot of time in the living room, watching videos. But I never suspected till they came to the bed that night. Then I knew; just a few seconds before she told me the baby was his, I knew. You know what would have been different? If I could have packed my things and walked out of the house. It would have hurt; it would have broken my heart; but it would have been different. On the day of my divorce it was summer, and it was raining. I couldn't get into the courthouse; I couldn't go up the steps. A guy was working a jackhammer on the sidewalk, about thirty yards away. The judge came down the steps in his robe, and we're all on the sidewalk, my wife, the lawyers. My lawyer's holding an umbrella over me. The jackhammer's going and I can't hear and I'm saying: 'What? What did he say?' Then I was divorced. I looked up at my wife, and asked her if she'd like Chinese lunch and a movie."

"*Why?*"

"I couldn't let go."

She reached and held his hand.

"Oh, Drew."

* * * * *

She did not know what time it was, and she did not look at the clock over the bar. There was no music. She sat beside Jeff. Drew had his sandwich in both hands; he bit it, then lowered it to the plate. Alvin was chewing; he looked at Drew; then as simply as if Drew's face were his own, he reached with a paper napkin and wiped mustard from Drew's chin. Drew glanced at him, and nodded. *That's how he says thank you,* Emily thought. One of a hundred ways he would have learned. She picked up her sandwich, looked across the table at Kay and Rita chewing small bites, looked to her right at Jeff's cheek bulging as he chewed. She ate, and drank. Kay said: "Let's go to my house, and dance all night."

"What about your neighbors?" Rita said.

"I don't have neighbors. I have a house."

"A whole house?"

"Roof. Walls. Lawn and trees."

"I haven't lived in a house since I grew up," Rita said.

"I've got to sleep," Drew said.

Alvin nodded.

"Me, too," Jeff said.

Rita said: "Not me. I'm off tomorrow."

"I won't play Sinatra," Kay said.

"He *is* good to dance to. You can play whatever you want."

Jeff and Alvin stood and cleared the table and took the plates and glasses to the kitchen. Drew moved his chair back from the table and went toward the door, and Emily stood and walked past him and opened the door. She stepped onto the landing, and smelled the ocean in the cool air; she looked up at stars. Then she watched Drew rolling out and turning down the ramp. Kay and Rita came, and Jeff and Alvin. Emily turned out the lights and locked the door and went with Jeff down the ramp. At the van, Emily turned to face the breeze, and looked up at the stars. She heard the sound of the lift and turned to see it coming out of the van. Kay leaned down and kissed Drew's cheek, and Rita did; they kissed Alvin's cheek, and Jeff shook his hand, then held Drew's hand and said: "Monday."

"We'll be here."

Emily took Alvin's hand and kissed his cheek. Jeff pointed east and told him how to drive to the motel. Emily held Drew's hands and leaned down and pressed her cheek against his; his face needed shaving. She straightened and watched Drew move backward onto the lift, then up into the van, where he turned and went to the passenger window. Alvin, calling good night, got into the van and started it and leaned over Drew and opened his window. Drew said: "Good night, sweet people."

Standing together, they all said good night and waved, held their hands up till Alvin turned the van and drove onto the road. Then Kay looked at Emily and Jeff.

"Come for just one drink."

Emily said: "I think it's even my bedtime. But ask me another night."

"And me," Jeff said.

"I will."

"I'll follow you," Rita said.

"It's not far."

They went to their cars, and Rita drove behind Kay, out of the parking lot, then west. Emily watched the red lights moving away, and felt tender, hopeful; she felt their hearts beating as they drove.

"Quite a night," she said.

"It's beautiful."

She looked at him; he was looking at the stars. She looked west again; the red lights rose over a hill and were gone. She looked at the sky.

"It is," she said. "That's not what I meant."

"I know. Do you think if Drew was up there hanging from a parachute, he could hear us?"

"I don't know."

He looked at his watch.

"You're right," he said. "It's four o'clock."

He walked beside her to her car; she unlocked it and opened the door, then turned to face him.

"I'm off Monday," she said. "I want to go fishing."

"Good."

She got into the car and closed the door and opened the window and looked up at Jeff.

"The bluefish are in," he said. "We'll catch some Monday."

"You already have some. Let's eat them for lunch."

"Today?"

"After we sleep. I don't know where you live."

"I'll call and tell you. At one?"

"One is fine," she said, and reached through the window and squeezed his hand. Then she drove east, smelling the ocean on the wind moving her hair.

THE RED CONVERTIBLE

L O U I S E   E R D R I C H

I was the first one to drive a convertible on my reservation. And of course it was red, a red Olds. I owned that car along with my brother Stephan. We owned it together until his boots filled with water on a windy night and he bought out my share. Now Stephan owns the whole car, and his younger brother Marty (that's myself) walks everywhere he goes.

How did I earn enough money to buy my share in the first place? My one talent was I could always make money. I had a touch for it, unusual in a Chippewa and especially in my family. From the first I was different that way and everyone recognized it. I was the only kid they let in the Rolla legion hall to shine shoes, for example, and one Christmas I sold spiritual bouquets for the Mission door-to-door. The nuns let me keep a percentage. Once I started, it seemed the more money I made the easier the money came. Everyone encouraged it. When I was fifteen I got a job washing dishes at the Joliet Café, and that was where my first big break came.

It wasn't long before I was promoted to busing tables, and then the short-order cook quit and I was hired to take her place. No sooner than you know it I was managing the Joliet. The rest is history. I went on managing. I soon became part-owner and of course there was no stopping me then. It wasn't long before the whole thing was mine.

After I'd owned the Joliet one year it burned down. The whole operation. I was only twenty. I had it all and I lost it quick, but before I lost it I had every one of my relatives, and their relatives, to dinner and I also bought that red Olds I mentioned, along with Stephan.

* * * * *

That time we first saw it! I'll tell you when we first saw it. We had gotten a ride up to Winnipeg and both of us had money. Don't ask me why because we never mentioned a car or anything, we just had all our money. Mine was cash, a big bankroll. Stephan had two checks—a week's extra pay for being laid off, and his regular check from the Jewel Bearing Plant.

We were walking down Portage anyway, seeing the sights, when we saw it. There it was, parked, large as alive. Really as *if* it was alive. I thought of the word "repose" because the car wasn't simply stopped, parked, or whatever. That car reposed, calm and gleaming, a FOR SALE sign in its left front window. Then before we had thought it over at all, the car belonged to us and our pockets were empty. We had just enough money for gas back home.

We went places in that car, me and Stephan. A little bit of insurance money came through from the fire and we took off driving all one whole summer. I can't tell you all the places we went to. We started off toward the Little Knife River and Mandaree in Fort Berthold and then we found ourselves down in Wakpala somehow and then suddenly we were over in Montana on the Rocky Boys and yet the summer was not even half over. Some people hang on to details when they travel, but we didn't let them bother us and just lived our everyday lives here to there.

I do remember there was this one place with willows; however, I laid under those trees and it was comfortable. So comfortable. The branches bent down all around me like a tent or a stable. And quiet, it was quiet, even though there was a dance close enough so I could see it going on. It was not too still, or too windy either, that day. When the dust rises up and hangs in the air around the dancers like that I feel comfortable. Stephan was asleep. Later on he woke up and we started driving again. We were somewhere in Montana, or maybe on the Blood Reserve, it could have been anywhere. Anyway it was where we met the girl.

* * * * *

All her hair was in buns around her ears, that's the first thing I saw. She was alongside the road with her arm out so we stopped. That girl was short, so short her lumber shirt looked comical on her, like a nightgown. She had jeans on and fancy moccasins and she carried a little suitcase.

"Hop on in," says Stephan. So she climbs in between us.

"We'll take you home," I says. "Where do you live?"

"Chicken," she says.

"Where's that?" I ask her.

"Alaska."

"Okay," Stephan says, and we drive.

We got up there and never wanted to leave. The sun doesn't truly set there in summer and the night is more a soft dusk. You might doze off, sometimes, but before you know it you're up again, like an animal in nature. You never feel like you have to sleep hard or put away the world. And things would grow up there. One day just dirt or moss, the next day flowers and long grass. The girl's family really took to us. They fed us and put us up. We had our own tent to live in by their house and the kids would be in and out of there all day and night.

One night the girl, Susy (she had another, longer name, but they called her Susy for short), came in to visit us. We sat around in the tent talking of this thing and that. It was getting darker by that time and the cold was even getting just a little mean. I told Susy it was time for us to go. She stood up on a chair.

"You never seen my hair," she said. That was true. She was standing on a chair, but still, when she unclipped her buns the hair reached all the way to the ground. Our eyes opened. You couldn't tell how much hair she had when it was rolled up so neatly. Then Stephan did something funny. He went up to the chair and said, "Jump on my shoulders." So she did that and her hair reached down past Stephan's waist and he started twirling, this way and that, so her hair was flung out from side to side.

"I always wondered what it was like to have long pretty hair," Stephan says! Well, we laughed. It was a funny sight, the way he did it. The next morning we got up and took leave of those people.

* * * * *

On to greener pastures, as they say. It was down through Spokane and across Idaho then Montana, and very soon we were racing the weather right along under the Canadian border through Columbus, Des Lacs, and then we were in Bottineau County and soon home. We'd made most of the trip, that summer, without putting up the car hood at all. We got home just in time, it turned out, for the army to remember Stephan had signed up to join it.

I don't wonder that the army was so glad to get Stephan that they turned him into a Marine. He was built like a brick outhouse anyway. We liked to tease him that they really wanted him for his Indian nose, though. He had a nose big and sharp as a hatchet. He had a nose like the nose on Red Tomahawk, the Indian who killed Sitting Bull, whose profile is on signs all along the North Dakota highways. Stephan went off to training camp, came home once during Christmas, then the next thing you know we got an overseas letter from Stephan. It was 1968, and he was stationed in Khe Sanh. I wrote him back several times. I kept him informed all about the car. Most of the time I had it up on blocks in the yard or half taken apart because that long trip wore out so much of it although, I must say, it gave us a beautiful performance when we needed it.

* * * * *

It was at least two years before Stephan came home again. They didn't want him back for a while, I guess, so he stayed on after Christmas. In those two years, I'd put his car into almost perfect shape. I always thought of it as his car, while he was gone, though when he left he said, "Now it's yours," and even threw me his key. "Thanks for the extra key," I said, "I'll put it up in your drawer just in case I need it." He laughed.

When he came home, though, Stephan was very different, and I'll say this, the change was no good. You could hardly expect him to change for the better; I know this. But he was quiet, so quiet, and never comfortable sitting still anywhere but always up and moving around. I thought back to times we'd sat still for whole afternoons, never moving, just shifting our weight along the ground, talking to whoever sat with us, watching things. He'd always had a joke then, too, and now you couldn't get him to laugh, or when he did it was more the sound of a man choking, a sound that stopped up the laughter in the throats of other people around him. They got to leaving him alone most of the time and I didn't blame them. It was a fact: Stephan was jumpy and mean.

I'd bought a color TV set for my mother and the kids while Stephan was away. (Money still came very easy.) I was sorry I'd ever bought it, though, because of Stephan, and I was also sorry I'd bought color because with black-and-white the pictures seem older and farther away. But what are you going to do? He sat in front of it, watching it, and that was the only time he was completely still. But it was the kind of stillness that you see in a rabbit when it freezes and before it will bolt. He was not comfortable. He sat in his chair gripping the armrests with all his might as if the chair itself was moving at a high speed, and if he let go at all he would rocket forward and maybe crash right through the set.

Once I was in the same room and I heard his teeth click at something. I looked over and he'd bitten through his lip. Blood was going down his chin. I tell you right then I wanted to smash that tube to pieces. I went over to it but Stephan must have known what I was up to. He rushed from his chair and shoved me out of the way, against the wall. I told myself he didn't know what he was doing.

My mother came in, turned the set off real quiet, and told us she had made something for supper. So we went and sat down. There was still blood going down Stephan's chin but he didn't notice it, and no one said anything even though every time he took a bite of his bread his blood fell onto it until he was eating his own blood mixed in with the food.

* * * * *

We talked, while Stephan was not around, about what was going to happen to him. There were no Indian doctors on the reservation, no medicine people, and my mother was afraid if we brought him to a regular hospital they would keep him. "No way would we get him there in the first place," I said, "so let's just forget about it." Then I thought about the car. Stephan had not even looked at the car since he'd gotten home, though like I said, it was in tip-top condition and ready to drive.

One night Stephan was off somewhere. I took myself a hammer. I went out to that car and I did a number on its underside. Whacked it up. Bent the tail pipe double. Ripped the muffler loose. By the time I was done with the car it looked worse than any typical Indian car that has been driven all its life on reservation roads which they always say are like government promises—full of holes. It just about hurt me, I'll tell you that! I threw dirt in the carburetor and I ripped all the electric tape off the seats.

I made it look just as beat up as I could. Then I sat back, and I waited for Stephan to find it.

Still, it took him over a month. That was all right because it was just getting warm enough, not melting but warm enough, to work outside, when he did find it.

"Marty," he says, walking in one day, "that red car looks like shit."

"Well it's old," I says. "You got to expect that."

"No way!" says Stephan. "That car's a classic! But you went and ran the piss right out of it, Marty, and you know it don't deserve that. I kept that car in A-one shape. You don't remember. You're too young. But when I left, that car was running like a watch. Now I don't even know if I can get it to start again, let alone get it anywhere near its old condition."

"Well, you try," I said, like I was getting mad, "but I say it's a piece of junk."

Then I walked out before he could realize I knew he'd strung together more than six words at once.

* * * * *

After that I thought he'd freeze himself to death working on that vehicle. I mean he was out there all day and at night he rigged up a little lamp, ran a cord out the window, and had himself some light to see by while he worked. He was better than he had been before, but that's still not saying much. It was easier for him to do the things the rest of us did. He ate more slowly and didn't jump up and down during the meal to get this or that or look out the window. I put my hand in the back of the TV set, I admit, and fiddled around with it good so that it was almost impossible now to get a clear picture. He didn't look at it very often. He was always out with that car or going off to get parts for it. By the time it was really melting outside, he had it fixed.

I had been feeling down in the dumps about Stephan around this time. We had always been together before. Stephan and Marty. But he was such a loner now I didn't know how to take it. So I jumped at the chance one day when Stephan seemed friendly. It's not that he smiled or anything. He just said, "Let's take that old shitbox for a spin." But just the way he said it made me think he could be coming around.

We went out to the car. It was spring. The sun was shining very bright. My little sister Bonita came out and made us stand together for a picture. He leaned his elbow on the red car's windshield and he took his other arm and put it over my shoulder, very carefully, as though it was heavy for him to lift and he didn't want to bring the weight down all at once. "Smile," Bonita said, and he did.

* * * * *

That picture. I never look at it anymore. A few months ago, I don't know why, I got his picture out and tacked it on my wall. I felt good about Stephan at the time, close to him. I felt good having his picture on the wall until one night when I was looking at television. I was a little drunk and stoned. I looked up at the wall and Stephan was staring at me. I don't know what it was but his smile had changed. Or maybe it was gone. All I know is I couldn't stay in the same room with that picture. I was shaking. I had to get up, close the door, and go into the kitchen. A little later my friend Rayman came and we both went back into that room. We put the picture in a bag and folded the bag over and over and put the picture way back in a closet.

I still see that picture now, as if it tugs at me, whenever I pass that closet door. It is very clear in my mind. It was so sunny that day, Stephan had to squint against the glare. Or maybe the camera Bonita held flashed like a mirror, blinding him, before she snapped the picture. My face is right out in the sun, big and round. But he might have drawn back a little because the shadows on his face are deep as holes. There are two shadows curved like little hooks around the ends of his smile as if to frame it and try to keep it there—that one, first smile that looked like it might have hurt his face. He has his field jacket on, and the worn-in clothes he'd come back in and kept wearing ever since. After Bonita took the picture and went into the house, we got into the car. There was a full cooler in the trunk. We started off, east, toward Pembina and the Red River because Stephan said he wanted to see the high water.

* * * * *

The trip over there was beautiful. When everything starts changing, drying up, clearing off, you feel so good it is like your whole life is starting. And Stephan felt it too. The top was down and the car hummed like a top. He'd really put it back in shape, even the tape on the seats was very carefully put down and glued back in layers. It's not that he smiled again or even joked or anything while we were driving, but his face looked to me as if it was clear, more peaceful. It looked as though he wasn't thinking of anything in particular except the blank fields and windbreaks and houses we were passing.

The river was high and full of winter trash when we got there. The sun was still out, but it was colder by the river. There were still little clumps of dirty snow here and there on the banks. The water hadn't gone over the banks yet, but it would, you could tell. It was just at its limit, hard, swollen, glossy like an old gray scar. We made ourselves a fire, and we sat down and watched the current go. As I watched it I felt something squeezing inside me and tightening and trying to let go all at the same time. I knew I was not just feeling it myself; I knew I was feeling what Stephan was going through at that moment. Except that Marty couldn't stand it, the feeling. I jumped to my feet. I took Stephan by the shoulders and I started shaking him. "Wake up," I says, "wake up, wake up, wake up!" I didn't know what had come over me. I sat down beside him again.

His face was totally white, hard, like a stone. Then it broke, like stones break all of the sudden when water boils up inside them.

"I know it," he says. "I know it. I can't help it. It's no use."

We started talking. He said he knew what I'd done with the car that time. It was obvious it had been whacked out of shape and not just neglected. He said he wanted to give the car to me for good now; it was no use. He said he'd fixed it just to give back and I should take it.

"No," I says, "I don't want it."

"That's okay," he says. "You take it."

"I don't want it though," I says back to him and then to emphasize, just to emphasize you understand, I touch his shoulder. He slaps my hand off.

"Take that car," he says.

"No," I say, "make me," I say, and then he grabs my jacket and rips the arm loose. I get mad and push him backwards, off the log. He jumps up and bowls me over. We go down in a clinch and come up swinging hard, for all we're worth, with our fists. He socks my jaw so hard I feel like it swings loose. Then I'm at his rib cage and land a good one under his chin so his head snaps back. He's dazzled. He looks at me and I look at him and then his eyes are full of tears and blood and he's crying I think at first. But no, he's laughing. "Ha! Ha!" he says. "Ha! Ha! Take good care of it!"

"Okay," I says. "Okay, no problem. Ha! Ha!"

I can't help it and I start laughing too. My face feels fat and strange and after a while I get a beer from the cooler in the trunk and when I hand it to Stephan he takes his shirt and wipes my germs off. "Hoof and mouth disease," he says. For some reason this cracks me up and so we're really laughing for a while then, and then we drink all the rest of the beers one by one and throw them in the river and see how far the current takes them, how fast, before they fill up and sink.

"I'm an Indian!" he shouts after a while.

"Whoo I'm on the lovepath! I'm out for loving!"

I think it's the old Stephan. He jumps up then and starts swinging his legs out from the knees like a fancydancer, then he's down doing something between a grouse dance and a bunny hop, no kind of dance I ever saw before but neither has anyone else on all this green growing earth. He's wild. He wants to pitch whoopee! He's up and at 'em and all over. All this time I'm laughing so hard, so hard my belly is getting tied up in a knot.

"Got to cool me off!" he shouts all of a sudden. Then he runs over to the river and jumps in.

There's boards and other things in the current. It's so high. No sound comes from the river after the splash he makes so I run right over. I look around. It's dark. I see he's halfway across the water already and I know he didn't swim there but the current took him. It's far. I hear his voice, though, very clearly across it.

"My boots are filling," he says.

He says this in a normal voice, like he just noticed and he doesn't know what to think of it. Then he's gone. A branch comes by. Another branch. By the time I get out of the river, off the snag I pulled myself onto, the sun is down. I walk back to the car, turn on the high beams, and drive it up the bank. I put it in first gear and then I take my foot off the clutch. I get out, close the door, and watch it plow softly into the water. The headlights reach in as they go down, searching, still lighted even after the water swirls over the back end. I wait. The wires short out. It is all finally dark. And then there is only the water, the sound of it going and running and going and running and running.

DESERT PLACES

ROBERT FROST

Snow falling and night falling fast, oh, fast
In a field I looked into going past,
And the ground almost covered smooth in snow,
But a few weeds and stubble showing last.

The woods around it have it—it is theirs.
All animals are smothered in their lairs.
I am too absent-spirited to count;
The loneliness includes me unawares.

And lonely as it is that loneliness
Will be more lonely ere it will be less—
A blanker whiteness of benighted snow
With no expression, nothing to express.

They cannot scare me with their empty spaces
Between stars—on stars where no human race is.
I have it in me so much nearer home
To scare myself with my own desert places.

AN OLD MAN'S WINTER NIGHT

ROBERT FROST

All out-of-doors looked darkly in at him
Through the thin frost, almost in separate stars,
That gathers on the pane in empty rooms.
What kept his eyes from giving back the gaze
Was the lamp tilted near them in his hand.
What kept him from remembering what it was
That brought him to that creaking room was age.
He stood with barrels round him—at a loss.
And having scared the cellar under him
In clomping here, he scared it once again
In clomping off;—and scared the outer night,
Which has its sounds, familiar, like the roar
Of trees and crack of branches, common things,
But nothing so like beating on a box.
A light he was to no one but himself
Where now he sat, concerned with he knew what,
A quiet light, and then not even that.
He consigned to the moon, such as she was,
So late-arising, to the broken moon
As better than the sun in any case
For such a charge, his snow upon the roof,
His icicles along the wall to keep;
And slept. The log that shifted with a jolt
Once in the stove, disturbed him and he shifted,
And eased his heavy breathing, but still slept.
One aged man—one man—can't keep a house,
A farm, a countryside, or if he can,
It's thus he does it of a winter night.

MY HEART IS BROKEN

MAVIS GALLANT

"When that Jean Harlow died," Mrs. Thompson said to Jeannie, "I was on the 83 streetcar with a big, heavy paper parcel in my arms. I hadn't been married for very long, and when I used to visit my mother she'd give me a lot of canned stuff and preserves. I was standing up in the streetcar because nobody'd given me a seat. All the men were unemployed in those days, and they just sat down wherever they happened to be. You wouldn't remember what Montreal was like then. *You* weren't even on earth. To resume what I was saying to you, one of these men sitting down had an American paper—the *Daily News,* I guess it was—and I was sort of leaning over him, and I saw in big print 'JEAN HARLOW DEAD.' You can believe me or not, just as you want to, but that was the most terrible shock I ever had in my life. I never got over it."

Jeannie had nothing to say to that. She lay flat on her back across the bed, with her head toward Mrs. Thompson and her heels just touching the crate that did as a bedside table. Balanced on her flat stomach was an open bottle of coral-pink Cutex nail polish. She held her hands up over her head and with some difficulty applied the brush to the nails of her right hand. Her legs were brown and thin. She wore nothing but shorts and one of her husband's shirts. Her feet were bare.

Mrs. Thompson was the wife of the paymaster in a road-construction camp in northern Quebec. Jeannie's husband was an engineer working on the same project. The road was being pushed through country where nothing had existed until now except rocks and lakes and muskeg. The camp was established between a wild lake and the line of raw dirt that was the road. There were no towns between the camp and the railway spur, sixty miles distant.

Mrs. Thompson, a good deal older than Jeannie, had become her best friend. She was a nice, plain, fat, consoling sort of person, with varicosed legs, shoes unlaced and slit for comfort, blue flannel dressing gown worn at all hours, pudding-bowl haircut, and coarse gray hair. She might have been Jeannie's own mother, or her Auntie Pearl. She rocked her fat self in the rocking chair and went on with what she had to say:

"What I was starting off to tell you is you remind me of her, of Jean Harlow. You've got the same teeny mouth, Jeannie, and I think your hair was a whole lot prettier before you started fooling around with it. That peroxide's no good. It splits the ends. I know you're going to tell me it isn't peroxide but something more modern, but the result is the same."

Vern's shirt was spotted with coral-pink that had dropped off the brush. Vern wouldn't mind; at least, he wouldn't say that he minded. If he hadn't objected to anything Jeannie did until now, he wouldn't start off by complaining about a shirt. The campsite outside the uncurtained window was silent and dark. The waning moon would not appear until dawn. A passage of thought made Mrs. Thompson say, "Winter soon."

Jeannie moved sharply and caught the bottle of polish before it spilled. Mrs. Thompson was crazy; it wasn't even September.

"Pretty soon," Mrs. Thompson admitted. "Pretty soon. That's a long season up here, but I'm one person doesn't complain. I've been up here or around here every winter of my married life, except for that one winter Pops was occupying Germany."

"I've been up here seventy-two days," said Jeannie, in her soft voice, "Tomorrow makes seventy-three."

"Is that right?" said Mrs. Thompson, jerking the rocker forward, suddenly snappish. "Is that a fact? Well, who asked you to come up here? Who asked you to come and start counting days like you was in some kind of jail? When you got married to Vern, you must of known where he'd be taking you. He told you, didn't he, that he liked road jobs, construction jobs, and that? Did he tell you, or didn't he?"

"Oh, he told me," said Jeannie.

"You know what, Jeannie?" said Mrs. Thompson. "If you'd of just listened to me, none of this would have happened. I told you that first day, the day you arrived here in your high-heeled shoes, I said, 'I know this cabin doesn't look much, but all the married men have the same sort of place.' You remember I said that? I said, 'You just get some curtains up and some carpets down and it'll be home.' I took you over and showed you my place, and you said you'd never seen anything so lovely."

"I meant it," said Jeannie. "Your cabin is just lovely. I don't know why, but I never managed to make this place look like yours."

Mrs. Thompson said, "That's plain enough." She looked at the cold grease spattered behind the stove, and the rag of towel over by the sink. "It's partly the experience," she said kindly. She and her husband knew exactly what to take with them when they went on a job, they had been doing it for so many years. They brought boxes for artificial flowers, a brass door knocker, a portable bar decorated with sea shells, a cardboard fireplace that looked real, and an electric fire that sent waves of light rippling over the ceiling and walls. A concealed gramophone played the records they loved and cherished—the good old tunes. They had comic records that dated back to the year 1, and sad soprano records about shipwrecks and broken promises and babies' graves. The first time Jeannie heard one of the funny records, she was scared to death. She was paying a formal call, sitting straight in her chair, with her skirt pulled around her knees. Vern and Pops Thompson were talking about the Army.

"I wish to God I was back," said old Pops.

"Don't I?" said Vern. He was fifteen years older than Jeannie and had been through a lot.

At first there were only scratching and whispering noises, and then a mosquito orchestra started to play, and a dwarf's voice came into the room. "Little Johnnie Green, little Sallie Brown," squealed the dwarf, higher and faster than any human ever could. "Spooning in the park with the grass all around."

"Where is he?" Jeannie cried, while the Thompsons screamed with laughter and Vern smiled. The dwarf sang on: "And each little bird in the treetop high/Sang 'Oh you kid!' and winked his eye."

It was a record that had belonged to Pops Thompson's mother. He had been laughing at it all his life. The Thompsons loved living up north and didn't miss cities or company. Their cabin smelled of cocoa and toast. Over their beds were oval photographs of each other as children, and they had some Teddy bears and about a dozen dolls.

* * * * *

Jeannie capped the bottle of polish, taking care not to press it against her wet nails. She sat up with a single movement and set the bottle down on the bedside crate. Then she turned to face Mrs. Thompson. She sat cross-legged, with her hands outspread before her. Her face was serene.

"Not an ounce of fat on you," said Mrs. Thompson. "You know something? I'm sorry you're going. I really am. Tomorrow you'll be gone. You know that, don't you? You've been counting days, but you won't have to any more. I guess Vern'll take you back to Montreal. What do you think?"

Jeannie dropped her gaze, and began smoothing wrinkles on the bedspread. She muttered something Mrs. Thompson could not understand.

"Tomorrow you'll be gone," Mrs. Thompson continued. "I know it for a fact. Vern is at this moment getting his pay, and borrowing a jeep from Mr. Sherman, and a Polack driver to take you to the train. He sure is loyal to *you*. You know what I heard Mr. Sherman say? He said to Vern, 'If you want to send her off, Vern, you can always stay,' and Vern said, 'I can't very well do that, Mr. Sherman.' And Mr. Sherman said, 'This is the second time you've had to leave a job on account of her, isn't it?,' and then Mr. Sherman said, 'In my opinion, no man by his own self can rape a girl, so there were either two men or else she's invented the whole story.' Then he said, 'Vern, you're either a saint or a damn fool.' That was all I heard. I came straight over here, Jeannie, because I thought you might be needing me." Mrs. Thompson waited to hear she was needed. She stopped rocking and sat with her feet flat and wide apart.

She struck her knees with her open palms and cried, "I *told* you to keep away from the men. I told you it would make trouble, all that being cute and dancing around. I said to you, I remember saying it, I said nothing makes trouble faster in a place like this than a grown woman behaving like a little girl. Don't you remember?"

"I only went out for a walk," said Jeannie. "Nobody'll believe me, but that's all. I went down the road for a walk."

"In high heels?" said Mrs. Thompson. "With a purse on your arm, and a hat on your head? You don't go taking a walk in the bush that way. There's no place to walk *to*. Where'd you think you were going? I could smell Evening in Paris a quarter mile away."

"There's no place to go," said Jeannie, "but what else is there to do? I just felt like dressing up and going out."

"You could have cleaned up your home a bit," said Mrs. Thompson. "There was always that to do. Just look at that sink. That basket of ironing's been under the bed since July. I know it gets boring around here, but you had the best of it. You had the summer. In winter it gets dark around three o'clock. Then the wives have a right to go crazy. I knew one used to sleep the clock around. When her Nembutal ran out, she took about a hundred aspirin. I knew another learned to distill her own liquor, just to kill time. Sometimes the men get so's they don't like the life, and that's death for the wives. But here you had a nice summer, and Vern liked the life."

"He likes it better than anything," said Jeannie. "He liked the Army, but this was his favorite life after that."

"There," said Mrs. Thompson. "You had every reason to be happy. What'd you do if he sent you off alone, now, like Mr. Sherman advised? You'd be alone and you'd have to work. Women don't know when they're well off. Here you've got a good, sensible husband working for you and you don't appreciate it. You have to go and do a terrible thing."

"I only went for a walk," said Jeannie. "That's all I did."

"It's possible," said Mrs. Thompson, "but it's a terrible thing. It's about the worst thing that's ever happened around here. I don't know why you let it happen. A woman can always defend what's precious, even if she's attacked. I hope you remember to think about bacteria."

"What d'you mean?"

"I mean Javelle, or something."

Jeannie looked uncomprehending and then shook her head.

"I wonder what it must be like," said Mrs. Thompson after a time, looking at the dark window. "I mean, think of Berlin and them Russians and all. Think of some disgusting fellow you don't know. Never said hello to, even. Some girls ask for it, though. You can't always blame the man. The man loses his job, his wife if he's got one, everything, all because of a silly girl."

Jeannie frowned, absently. She pressed her nails together, testing the polish. She licked her lips and said, "I was more beaten up, Mrs. Thompson. It wasn't exactly what you think. It was only afterwards I thought to myself, Why, I was raped and everything."

Mrs. Thompson gasped, hearing the word from Jeannie. She said, "Have you got any marks?"

"On my arms. That's why I'm wearing this shirt. The first thing I did was change my clothes."

Mrs. Thompson thought this over, and went on to another thing: "Do you ever think about your mother?"

"Sure."

"Do you pray? If this goes on at nineteen—"

"I'm twenty."

"—what'll you be by the time you're thirty? You've already got a terrible, terrible memory to haunt you all your life."

"I already can't remember it," said Jeannie. "Afterwards I started walking back to camp, but I was walking the wrong way. I met Mr. Sherman. The back of his car was full of coffee, flour, all that. I guess he'd been picking up supplies. He said, 'Well, get in.' He didn't ask any questions at first. I couldn't talk anyway."

"Shock," said Mrs. Thompson wisely.

"You know, I'd have to see it happening to know what happened. All I remember is that first we were only talking…"

"You and Mr. Sherman?"

"No, no, before. When I was taking my walk."

"Don't say who it was," said Mrs. Thompson. "We don't any of us need to know."

"We were just talking, and he got sore all of a sudden and grabbed my arm."

"Don't say the name!" Mrs. Thompson cried.

"Like when I was little, there was this Lana Turner movie. She had two twins. She was just there and then a nurse brought her in the two twins. I hadn't been married or anything, and I didn't know anything, and I used to think if I just kept on seeing the movie I'd know how she got the two twins, you know, and I went, oh, I must have seen it six times, the movie, but in the end I never knew any more. They just brought her the two twins."

Mrs. Thompson sat quite still, trying to make sense of this. "Taking advantage of a woman is a criminal offense," she observed. "I heard Mr. Sherman say another thing, Jeannie. He said, 'If your wife wants to press a charge and talk to some lawyer, let me tell you,' he said, 'you'll never work again anywhere,' he said. Vern said, 'I know that, Mr. Sherman.' And Mr. Sherman said, 'Let me tell you, if any reporters or any investigators start coming around here, they'll get their…they'll never…' Oh, he was mad. And Vern said, 'I came over to tell you I was quitting, Mr. Sherman.'" Mrs. Thompson had been acting this with spirit, using a quiet voice when she spoke for her Vern and a blustering tone for Mr. Sherman. In her own voice, she said, "If you're wondering how I came to hear all this, I was strolling by Mr. Sherman's office window—his bungalow, that is. I had Maureen out in her pram." Maureen was the Thompson's youngest doll.

Jeannie might not have been listening. She started to tell something else: "You know, where we were before, on Vern's last job, we weren't in a camp. He was away a lot, and he left me in Amos, in a hotel. I liked it. Amos isn't all that big, but it's better than here. There was this German in the hotel. He was selling cars. He'd drive me around if I wanted to go to a movie or anything. Vern didn't like him, so we left. It wasn't anybody's fault."

"So he's given up two jobs," said Mrs. Thompson. "One because he couldn't leave you alone, and now this one. Two jobs, and you haven't been married five months. Why should another man be thrown out of work? We don't need to know a thing. I'll be sorry if it was Jimmy Quinn," she went on, slowly. "I like that boy. Don't say the name, dear. There's Evans. Susini. Palmer. But it might have been anybody, because you had them all on the boil. So it might have been Jimmy Quinn—let's say—and it could have been anyone else, too. Well, now let's hope they can get there minds back on the job."

"I thought they all liked me," said Jeannie sadly. "I get along with people. Vern never fights with me."

"Vern never fights with anyone. But he ought to have thrashed *you*."

"If he…you know. I won't say the name. If he'd liked me, I wouldn't have minded. If he'd been friendly. I really mean that. I wouldn't have gone wandering up the road, making all this fuss."

"Jeannie," said Mrs. Thompson, "you don't even know what you're saying."

"He could have at least have liked me," said Jeannie. "He wasn't even friendly. It's the first time in my life somebody hasn't liked me. My heart is broken, Mrs. Thompson. My heart is just broken."

She has to cry, Mrs. Thompson thought. She has to have it out. She rocked slowly, tapping her foot, trying to remember how she'd felt about things when she was twenty, wondering if her heart had ever been broken, too.

WOUNDED SOLDIER (CARTOON STRIP)

GEORGE GARRETT

When the time came at last and they removed the wealth of bandages from his head and face, all with the greatest of care as if they were unwinding a precious mummy, the Doctor—he of the waxed, theatrical, upswept mustache and the wet sad eyes of a beagle hound—turned away. Orderlies and aides coughed, looked at floor and ceiling, busied themselves with other tasks. Only the Head Nurse, a fury stiff with starch and smelling of strong soap, looked, pink-cheeked and pale white as fresh flour, over the Veteran's shoulders. She stared back at him, unflinching and expressionless, from the swimming light of the mirror.

No question. It was a terrible wound.

– I'm so sorry, the Doctor said. – It's the best we can do for you.

But the Veteran barely heard his words. The Veteran looked deeply into the mirror and stared at the stranger, who was now to be himself, with an inward wincing that was nearer to the sudden gnawing of love at first sight than of self-pity. It was like being born again. He had, after all, not seen himself since the blinding, burning instant when he was wounded. Ever since then he had been a mystery to himself. How many times he had stared into the mirror through the neat little slits left for his eyes and seen only a snowy skull of gauze and bandages! He imagined himself as a statue waiting to be unveiled. And now he regretted that there was no real audience for the occasion except for the Doctor, who would not look, and the Head Nurse—she for whom no truth could be veiled anyway and hence for whom there could never be any system or subtle aesthetic of exposure or disclosure by any clever series of gradual deceptions. She carried the heavy burden of one who was familiar with every imaginable kind of wound and deformity.

– You're lucky to be alive, she said. – Really lucky.

– I don't know what you will want to do with yourself, the Doctor said. – Of course, you understand that you are welcome to remain here.

– That might be the best thing for any number of good reasons, the Head Nurse said. Then to the Doctor: – Ordinarily cases like this one elect to remain in the hospital.

– Are there others? the Veteran asked.

– Well…the Head Nurse admitted, there are none quite like you.

– I should hope not, the Veteran said, suddenly laughing at himself in the mirror. – Under the circumstances it's only fair that I should be able to feel unique.

– I am so sorry, the Doctor said.

Over the Veteran's shoulder in the mirror the Head Nurse smiled back at him.

That same afternoon a High-ranking Officer came to call on him. The Officer kept his eyes fixed on the glossy shine of his boots. After mumbled amenities he explained to the Veteran that while the law certainly allowed him to be a free man, free to come and go as he might choose, he ought to give consideration to the idea that his patriotic duty had not ended with the misfortune of his being stricken in combat. There were, the Officer explained, certain abstract obligations that clearly transcended those written down as statute law and explicitly demanded by the State.

– There are duties, he continued, waxing briefly poetic, which like certain of the cardinal virtues, are deeply disguised. Some of these are truly sublime. Some are rare and splendid like the aroma of a dying arrangement of flowers or the persistent haunting of half-remembered melodies.

The Veteran, who knew something about the music of groans and howls, and something about odors, including, quite recently, the stink of festering and healing, was not to be deceived by this sleight of hand.

– Get to the point, he said.

The High-ranking Officer was flustered, for he was not often addressed by anyone in this fashion. He stammered, spluttered as he offered the Veteran a bonus to his regular pension, a large sum of money, should he freely choose to remain here in the hospital. After all, his care and maintenance would be excellent and he would be free of many commonplace anxieties. Moreover, he need never feel that his situation was anything like being a prisoner. The basic truth about any prisoner is—is it not?—that he is to be deliberately deprived, insofar as possible, of all the usual objects of desire. The large bonus would enable the Veteran to live well, even lavishly in the hospital if he wanted to.

– Why?

Patiently the Officer pointed out that his appearance in public, in the city or the country, would probably serve to arouse the anguish of the civilian population. So many among the military personnel had been killed or wounded in this most recent war. Wasn't it better for everyone concerned, especially the dependents, the friends and relatives of these unfortunate men, that they be permitted to keep their innocent delusions of swirling battle flags and dimly echoing bugle calls, rather than being forced to confront in fact and flesh the elemental brute ugliness of modern warfare? As an old soldier, or as one old soldier to another, surely the Veteran must and would acknowledge the validity of this argument.

The Veteran nodded and replied that he guessed the Officer also hadn't overlooked the effect his appearance might have on the young men of the nation. Most likely a considerable cooling of patriotic ardor. Probably a noticeable, indeed a measurable, decline in the number of enlistments.

– Just imagine for a moment, the Veteran said, what it would be like if I went out there and stood right next to the recruiting poster at the Post Office. Sort of like a "before and after" advertisement.

At this point the Officer stiffened, scolded, and threatened. He ended by reminding the Veteran that no man, save the One, had ever been perfect and blameless. He suggested to him that, under the strictest scrutiny, his service record would no doubt reveal some error or other, perhaps some offense committed while he was a soldier on active duty, which would still render him liable to a court-martial prosecution.

Safe for the time being with his terrible wound, the Veteran laughed out loud and told the Officer that nothing they could do or think of doing to him could ever equal this. That he might as well waste his time trying to frighten a dead man or violate a corpse.

Then the Officer pleaded with the Veteran. He explained that his professional career as a leader of men might be ruined if he failed in the fairly simple assignment of convincing one ordinary common soldier to do as he was told to.

The Veteran, pitying this display of naked weakness, said that he would think about it very seriously. With that much accomplished, the Officer brightened and recovered his official demeanor.

– I imagine it would have been so much more convenient for everyone if I had simply been killed, wouldn't it? the Veteran asked as the Officer was leaving.

Still bowed, still unable to look at him directly, the Officer shrugged his epauleted shoulders and closed the door very quietly behind him.

* * * * *

Nevertheless the Veteran had made up his mind to leave the sanctuary of the hospital. Despite his wound and appearance, he was in excellent health, young still and full of energy. And the tiptoeing routine of this place was ineffably depressing. Yet even though he had decided to leave, even though he was certain he was going soon, he lingered, he delayed, he hesitated. Days went by quietly and calmly, and in the evening when she was off duty, the Head Nurse often came to his room to talk to him about things. Often they played cards. A curious and easy intimacy developed. It seemed almost as if they were husband and wife. On one occasion he spoke to her candidly about this.

– You better be careful, he said. – I'm not sexless.

– No, I guess not, she said. – But I am.

She told him that she thought his plan of going out into the world again was dangerous and foolish.

– Go ahead. Try it and you'll be back here in no time at all, beating on the door with bloody knuckles and begging to be readmitted, to get back in. You are too young and inexperienced to understand anything about people. Human beings are the foulest things in all creation. They will smell your blood and go mad like sharks. They will kill you if they can. They can't allow you to be out there among them. They will tear you limb from limb. They will strip the meat off your bones and trample your bones to dust. They will turn you into dust and a fine powder and scatter you to the four winds!

– I can see you have been deeply wounded, too, the Veteran said.

At that the Head Nurse laughed out loud. Her whole white mountainous body shook with laughter.

* * * * *

When the Veteran left the hospital, he wore a mask. He wanted to find a job, and wearing the mask seemed to him to be an act of discretion that would be appreciated. But this, as he soon discovered, was not the case at all. A mask is somehow intolerable. A mask becomes an unbearable challenge. When he became aware of this, when he had considered it, only the greatest exercise of self-discipline checked within him the impulse to gratify their curiosity. It would have been so easy. He could so easily have peeled off his protective mask and thereby given to the ignorant and innocent a new creature for their bad dreams.

One day he came upon a small traveling circus and applied for a job with them.

– What can you do? the Manager asked.

This Manager was a man so bowed down by the weight of weariness and boredom that he seemed at first glance to be a hunchback. He had lived so long and so closely with the oddly gifted and with natural freaks that his lips were pursed as if to spit in contempt at everything under the sun.

– I can be a clown, the Veteran said.

– I have enough clowns, the Manager said. Frankly, I am sick to death of clowns.

– I'll be different from any other clown you have ever seen, the Veteran said.

And then and there he took off his mask.

– Well, this is highly original, the Manager said, studying the crude configuration of the wound with a careful, pitiless interest. This has some definite possibilities.

– I suppose the real question is, will the people laugh?

– Without a doubt. Believe me. Remember this—a man is just as apt to giggle when he is introduced to his executioner as he is to melt into a mess of piss and fear. The real and true talent, the exquisite thing, is of course to be able to raise tears to the throat and to the rims of the eyes, and then suddenly to convert those tears into laughter.

– I could play "The Wounded Soldier."

– Well, we'll try it, the Manager said. I think it's worth a try.

And so that same night he first appeared in his new role. He entered with all the other clowns. The other clowns were conventional. They wore masks and elaborate makeup, sported baggy trousers and long, upturned shoes. They smoked exploding cigars. They flashed red electric noses on and off. They gamboled like a blithe flock of stray lambs, unshepherded. The Veteran, however, merely entered with them and then walked slowly around the ring. He wore a battered tin helmet and a uniform a generation out-of-date with its old-fashioned, badly wrapped puttees and a high, choker collar. He carried a broken stub of a rifle, hanging in two pieces like an open shotgun. A touch of genius, the Manager had attached a large clump of barbed wire to the seat of his pants.

The Veteran was seriously worried that people would not laugh at him and that he wouldn't be able to keep his job. Slowly, apprehensively, he strolled around the enormous circle and turned his wound toward them. He could see nothing at all outside of the zone of light surrounding him. But it was not long before he heard a great gasp from the outer darkness, a shocked intaking of breath so palpable that it was like a sudden breeze. And then he heard the single, high-pitched, hysterical giggle of a woman. And next came all that indrawn air returning, rich and warm. The whole crowd laughed at once. The crowd laughed loudly and the tent seemed to swell like a full sail from their laughter. He could see the circus bandsmen puffing like bullfrogs as they played their instruments and could see the sweat-stained leader waving his baton in a quick, strict, martial time. But he could not hear the least sound of their music. It was engulfed, drowned out, swallowed up by the raging storm of laughter.

Soon afterwards the Veteran signed a contract with the circus. His name was placed prominently on all the advertising posters and materials together with such luminaries as the Highwire Walker, the Trapeze Artists, the Lion Tamer, and the Bareback Riders. He worked only at night. For he soon discovered that by daylight he could see his audience, and they knew that and either refused to laugh or were unable to do so under the circumstances. He concluded that only when they were in the relative safety of the dark would they give themselves over to the impulse of laughter.

His fellow clowns, far from being envious of him, treated him with the greatest respect and admiration. And before much time had passed, he had received the highest compliment from a colleague in that vocation. A clown in a rival circus attempted an imitation of his art. But this clown was not well received. In fact, he was pelted with peanuts and hot dogs, with vegetables and fruit and rotten eggs and bottles. He was jeered at and catcalled out of the ring. Because no amount of clever makeup could rival or compete with the Veteran's unfortunate appearance.

Once a beautiful young woman came to the trailer where he lived and prepared for his performance. She told him that she loved him.

– I have seen every single performance since the first night, she said. I want to be with you always.

The Veteran was not unmoved by her beauty and her naïveté. Besides, he had been alone for quite a long time.

— I'm afraid you don't realize what you are saying, he told her.

— If you won't let me be your mistress, I am going to kill myself, she said.

— That would be a pity.

She told him that more than anything else she wanted to have a child by him.

— If we have a child, then I'll have to marry you.

— Do you think, she asked, that our child would look like you?

— I don't believe that is scientifically possible, he said.

Later when she bore his child, it was a fine healthy baby, handsome and glowing. And then, as inexplicably as she had first come to him, the young woman left him.

After a few successful seasons, the Veteran began to lose some of his ability to arouse laughter from the public. By that time almost all of them had seen him at least once already, and the shock had numbed their responses. Perhaps some of them had begun to pity him.

The Manager was concerned about his future.

— Maybe you should take a rest, go into a temporary retirement, he said. People forget everything very quickly nowadays. You could come back to clowning in no time.

— But what would I ever do with myself?

The Manager shrugged.

— You could live comfortably on your savings and your pension, he said. Don't you have any hobbies or outside interests?

— But I really like it here, the Veteran said. Couldn't I wear a disguise and be one of the regular clowns?

— It would take much too long to learn the tricks of the trade, the Manager said. Besides which your real clowns are truly in hiding. Their whole skill lies in the concealment of anguish. And your talent is all a matter of revelation.

It was not long after this conversation that the Veteran received a letter from the Doctor.

— Your case has haunted me and troubled me, night and day, the Doctor wrote. I have been studying the problem incessantly. And now I think I may be able to do something for you. I make no promises, but I think I can help you. Could you return to the hospital for a thorough examination?

While he waited for the results of all the tests, the Veteran lived in his old room. It was clean and bright and quiet as before. Daily the Head Nurse put a bouquet of fresh flowers in a vase by his bed.

— You may be making a big mistake, she told him. You have lived too long with your wound. Even if the Doctor is successful—and he may be, for he is extremely skillful—you'll never be happy with yourself again.

— Do you know? he began. I was very happy being a clown. For the first and only time in my life all that I had to do was to be myself. But, of course, like everything else, it couldn't last for long.

– You can always come back here. You can stay just as you are now.

– Would you be happy, he asked her, if I came back to the hospital for good just as I am now?

– Oh yes, she said. I believe I would be very happy.

Nevertheless the Veteran submitted to the Doctor's treatment. Once again he became a creature to be wheeled into the glaring of harsh lights, to be surrounded and hovered over by intense masked figures. Once again he was swathed in white bandages and had to suffer through a long time of healing, waiting for the day when he would see himself again. Once again the momentous day arrived, and he stood staring into a mirror as they unwound his bandages.

This time, when the ceremony was completed, he looked into the eyes of a handsome stranger.

– You cannot possibly imagine, the Doctor said, what this moment means to me.

The Head Nurse turned away and could not speak to him.

* * * * *

When he was finally ready to leave the hospital, the Veteran found the High-ranking Officer waiting for him. A gleaming staff car was parked at the curb, and the Veteran noticed by his insignia that the Officer had been promoted.

– We all hope, the Officer said, that you will seriously consider returning to active duty. We need experienced men more than ever now.

– That's a very kind offer, the Veteran said. And I'll certainly consider it in all seriousness.

CASUALTIES OF WAR

ATUL GAWANDE

Each Tuesday, the U.S. Department of Defense provides an online update of American military casualties from the wars in Iraq and Afghanistan. According to this update, as of December 8, 2006, a total of 26,547 service members had suffered battle injuries. Of these, 2,662 died; 10,839 lived but could not return to duty; and 13,085 were less severely wounded and returned to duty within seventy-two hours. These figures represent, by a considerable margin, the largest burden of casualties our military medical personnel have had to cope with since the Vietnam War.

When U.S. combat deaths in Iraq reached the two-thousand mark in September 2005, the event captured worldwide attention. Combat deaths are seen as a measure of the magnitude and dangerousness of war, just as murder rates are seen as a measure of the magnitude and dangerousness of violence in our communities. Both, however, are weak proxies. Little recognized is how fundamentally important the medical system is—and not just the enemy's weaponry—in determining whether or not someone dies. U.S. homicide rates, for example, have dropped in recent years to levels unseen since the mid-1960s. Yet aggravated assaults, particularly with firearms, have more than tripled during that period. A key mitigating factor appears to be the trauma care provided: more people may be getting shot, but doctors are saving even more of them. Mortality from gun assaults has fallen from 16 percent in 1964 to 5 percent today.

We have seen a similar evolution in war. Though firepower has increased, lethality has decreased. In the Revolutionary War, American soldiers faced bayonets and single-shot rifles, and 42 percent of the battle wounded died. In World War II, American soldiers were hit with grenades, bombs, shells, and machine guns, yet only 30 percent of the wounded died. By the Korean War, the weaponry was certainly no less terrible, but the mortality rate for combat-injured soldiers fell to 25 percent.

Over the next half century, we saw little further progress. Through the Vietnam War (with its 153,303 combat wounded and 47,424 combat dead) and even the 1990-91 Persian Gulf War (with its 467 wounded and 147 dead), mortality rates for the battle injured remained at 24 percent. Our technology to save the wounded seemed to have barely kept up with the technology inflicting the wounds.

The military wanted desperately to find ways to do better. The most promising approach was to focus on discovering new treatments and technologies. In the previous century, that was where progress had been found—in the discovery of new anesthetic agents and vascular surgery techniques for World War I soldiers, in the development of better burn treatments, blood transfusion methods, and penicillin for World War II soldiers, in the availability of a broad range of antibiotics for Korean War soldiers. The United States accordingly invested hundreds of millions of dollars in numerous new possibilities: the development of blood substitutes and freeze-dried plasma (for infusion when fresh blood is not available), gene therapies for traumatic wounds, medications to halt lung injury, miniaturized systems to monitor and transmit the vital signs of soldiers in the field.

Few if any of these have yet come to fruition, however, and none were responsible for what we have seen in the current wars in Iraq and Afghanistan: a marked, indeed historic, reduction in the lethality of battle wounds. Although more U.S. soldiers have been wounded in combat in the current war than in the Revolutionary War, the War of 1812, and the Spanish-American War combined, and more than in the first four years of military involvement in Vietnam, we have had substantially fewer deaths. Just 10 percent of wounded Americans soldiers have died.

How military medical teams have achieved this is important to think about. They have done it despite having no fundamentally new technologies or treatments since the Persian Gulf War. And they have done it despite difficulties with the supply of medical personnel. For its entire worldwide mission, the army had only about 120 general surgeons available on active duty and two hundred in the reserves in 2005. To support the 130,000 to 150,000 troops fighting in Iraq, it has been able to put no more than thirty to fifty general surgeons and ten to fifteen orthopedic surgeons on the ground. And these surgeons and their teams have been up against devastating injuries.

I got a sense of the extent of the injuries during a visit to Walter Reed Army Medical Center in Washington, D.C., in the fall of 2004, when I was invited to sit in on what the doctors call their "War Rounds." Every Thursday, the Walter Reed surgeons hold a telephone conference with army surgeons in Baghdad to review the American casualties received in Washington. The case list for discussion the day I visited included one gunshot wound, one antitank-mine injury, one grenade injury, three rocket-propelled-grenade injuries, four mortar injuries, eight improvised explosive device (IED) injuries, and seven with no cause of injury noted. None of these soldiers was more than twenty-five years of age. The least seriously wounded was a nineteen-year-old who had sustained extensive blast and penetrating injuries to his face and neck from a mine. Other cases included a soldier with a partial hand amputation; one with a massive blast injury that amputated his right leg at the hip, a through-knee amputation of his left leg, and an open pelvic wound; one with bullet wounds to his left kidney and colon; one with bullet wounds under his arm requiring axillary artery and vein reconstruction; and one with a shattered spleen, a degloving scalp laceration, and a through-and-through tongue laceration. These are terrible and formidable injuries. Nonetheless, all were saved.

* * * * *

If the answer to how was not to be found in new technologies, it did not seem to reside in any special skills of military doctors, either. George Peoples is a forty-two-year-old surgical oncologist who was my chief resident when I was a surgical intern. In October 2001, after the September 11 attacks on the World Trade Center and the Pentagon, he led the first surgical team into Afghanistan. He returned after service there only to be sent to Iraq, in March 2003, with ground forces invading from Kuwait through the desert to Baghdad. He had gone to the U.S. Military Academy at West Point for college, Johns Hopkins Medical School in Baltimore, Brigham and Women's Hospital in Boston for surgical residency, and then M.D. Anderson Cancer Center in Houston for a cancer surgery fellowship. He owed the army eighteen years of service when he finally finished his training, and neither I nor anyone I know ever heard him bemoan that commitment. In 1998, he was assigned to Walter Reed, where he practiced surgical oncology. Peoples was known in training for three things: his unflappability, his intellect (he had published seventeen papers on work toward a breast cancer vaccine before he finished his training), and the five children he and his wife had during his residency. He was not known, however, for any particular expertise in trauma surgery. Before being deployed, he hadn't seen a gunshot wound since residency, and even then, he never saw anything like the injuries he saw in Iraq. His practice at Walter Reed centered on breast surgery. Yet in Iraq, he and his team managed to save historic numbers of wounded.

"How is this possible?" I asked him. I asked his colleagues, too. I asked everyone I met who had worked on medical teams in the war. And what they described revealed an intriguing effort to do something we in civilian medicine do spottily at best: to make a science of performance, to investigate and improve how well they use the knowledge and technologies they already have at hand. The doctors told me of simple, almost banal changes that produced enormous improvements.

One such change involved Kevlar vests, for example. There is nothing new about Kevlar. It has been around since the late 1970s. Urban police forces began using Kevlar vests in the early 1980s. American troops had them during the Persian Gulf War. A sixteen-pound Kevlar flak vest will protect a person's "body core"—the heart, the lungs, the abdominal organs—from blasts, blunt force trauma, and penetrating injuries. But researchers examining wound registries from the Persian Gulf War found that wounded soldiers had been coming in to medical facilities without their Kevlar on. *They hadn't been wearing their vests.* So orders were handed down holding commanders responsible for ensuring that their soldiers always wore the vests—however much they might complain about how hot or heavy or uncomfortable the vests were. Once the soldiers began wearing them more consistently, the percentage killed on the battlefield dropped instantly.

A second, key discovery came in much the same way, by looking more carefully at how the system was performing. Colonel Ronald Bellamy, a surgeon with the army's Bordon Institute, examined the statistics of the Vietnam War and found that helicopter evacuation had reduced the transport time for injured soldiers to hospital care from an average of over eleven hours in World War II to under an hour. And once they got to surgical care, only 3 percent died. Yet 24 percent of wounded soldiers died in all, and that was because transport time to surgical care under an hour still wasn't fast enough. Civilian surgeons talk of having a "Golden Hour" during which most trauma victims can be saved if treatment is started. But battlefield injuries are so much more severe—the blood loss in particular—that wounded soldiers have only a "Golden Five Minutes," Bellamy reported. Vests could extend those five minutes. But the recent emphasis on leaner, faster-moving military units moving much farther ahead of supply lines and medical facilities was only going to make evacuation to medical care more difficult and time-consuming. Outcomes for the wounded were in danger of getting worse rather than better.

The army therefore turned to an approach that had been used in isolated instances going back as far as World War II: something called Forward Surgical Teams (FSTs). These are small teams, consisting of just twenty people: three general surgeons, one orthopedic surgeon, two nurse anesthetists, three nurses, plus medics and other support personnel. In Iraq and Afghanistan, they travel in six Humvees directly behind the troops, right out onto the battlefield. They carry three lightweight, Deployable Rapid-Assembly Shelter ("drash") tents that attached to one another to form a nine-hundred-square-foot hospital facility. Supplies to immediately resuscitate and operate on the wounded are in five black nylon backpacks: an ICU pack, a surgical-technician pack, an anesthesia pack, a general-surgery pack, and an orthopedic pack. They hold sterile instruments, anesthesia equipment, medicines, drapes, gowns, catheters, and a handheld unit that allows clinicians to measure a complete blood count, electrolytes, or blood gases with a drop of blood. FSTs also carry a small ultrasound machine, portable monitors, transport ventilators, an oxygen concentrator providing up to 50 percent pure oxygen, twenty units of packed red blood cells for transfusion, and six roll-up stretchers with litter stands. All of this is ordinary medical equipment. The teams must forgo many technologies normally available to a surgeon, such as angiography and radiography equipment. (Orthopedic surgeons, for example, have to detect fractures by feel.) But they can go from rolling to having a fully functioning hospital with two operating tables and four ventilator-equipped recovery beds in under sixty minutes.

Peoples led the 274th FST, which traveled 1,100 miles with troops during the invasion of Iraq. The team set up in Nasiriyah, Najaf, Karbala, and points along the way in the southern desert, then in Mosul in the north, and finally in Baghdad. According to its logs, the unit cared for 132 U.S. and 74 Iraqi casualties (22 of the Iraqis were combatants, 52 civilians) over those initial weeks. Some days were quiet, others overwhelming. On one day in Nasiriyah, the team received ten critically wounded soldiers, among them one with right-lower-extremity shrapnel injuries; one with gunshot wounds to the stomach, small bowel, and liver; another with gunshot wounds to the gallbladder, liver, and transverse colon; one with shrapnel in the neck, chest, and back; one with a gunshot wound through the rectum; and two with extremity gunshot wounds. The next day, fifteen more casualties arrived.

Peoples described to me how radically the new system changed the way he and his team took care of the wounded. On the arrival of the wounded, they carried out the standard Advanced Trauma Life Support protocols that all civilian trauma teams follow. However, because of the high proportion of penetrating wounds—80 percent of casualties seen by the 274th FST had gunshot wounds, shrapnel injuries, or blast injuries—lifesaving operative management is required far more frequently than in civilian trauma centers. The FST's limited supplies provided only for a short period of operative care for a soldier and no more than six hours of postoperative intensive care. So the unit's members focused on damage control, not definitive repair. They packed off liver injuries with gauze pads to stop the bleeding, put temporary plastic tubes in bleeding arteries to shunt the blood past the laceration, stapled off perforated bowel, washed out dirty wounds—whatever was necessary to control contamination and stop hemorrhage. They sought to keep their operations under two hours in length. Then, having stabilized the injuries, they shipped the soldier off—often still anesthetized, on a ventilator, the abdominal wound packed with gauze and left open, bowel loops not yet connected, blood vessels still needing repair—to another team at the next level of care.

They had available to them two Combat Support Hospitals (or CSHs—"CaSHes" —as they call them) in four locations for that next level of care. These are 248-bed hospitals typically with six operating tables, some specialty surgery services, and radiology and laboratory facilities. Mobile hospitals as well, they arrive in modular units by air, tractor trailer, or ship and can be fully functional in twenty-four to forty-eight hours. Even at the CSH level, the goal is not necessarily definitive repair. The maximal length of stay is intended to be three days. Wounded American soldiers requiring longer care are transferred to what's called a level IV hospital—one was established in Kuwait and one in Rota, Spain, but the main one is in Landstuhl, Germany. Those expected to require more than thirty days of treatment are transferred home, mainly to Walter Reed or to Brooke Army Medical Center in San Antonio, Texas. Iraqi prisoners and civilians, however, remain in the CSHs through recovery.

The system took some getting used to. Surgeons at every level initially tended to hold on to their patients, either believing that they could provide definitive care themselves or not trusting that the next level could do so. ("Trust no one" is the mantra we all learn to live by in surgical training.) According to statistics from Walter Reed, during the first few months of the war it took the most severely injured soldiers—those who clearly needed prolonged and extensive care—an average of eight days to go from the battlefield to a U.S. facility. Gradually, however, surgeons embraced the wisdom of the approach. The average time from battlefield to arrival in the United States is now less than four days. (In Vietnam, it was forty-five days.) And the system has worked.

One airman I met during my visit to Washington had experienced a mortar attack outside Balad on September 11, 2004, and ended up on a Walter Reed operating table just thirty-six hours later. In extremis from bilateral thigh injuries, abdominal wounds, shrapnel in the right hand, and facial injuries, he was taken from the field to the nearby 31st CSH in Balad. Bleeding was controlled, resuscitation with intravenous fluids and blood begun, a guillotine amputation at the thigh performed. He received exploratory abdominal surgery and, because a ruptured colon was found, a colostomy. His abdomen was left open, with a clear plastic covering sewn on. A note was taped to him explaining exactly what the surgeons had done. He was then taken to Landstuhl by an air force critical care transport team. When he arrived in Germany, Army surgeons determined that he would require more than thirty days of recovery, if he made it at all. Resuscitation was continued, a quick further washout performed, and then he was sent on to Walter Reed. There, after weeks in intensive care and multiple operations to complete the repairs, he survived. This sequence of care is unprecedented, and so is the result. Injuries like his were unsurvivable in previous wars.

But if mortality is low, the human cost remains high. The airman lost one leg above the knee, the other at the hip, his right hand, and part of his face. How he and others like him will be able to live and function remains an open question. His abdominal injuries prevented him from being able to lift himself out of bed or into a wheelchair. With only one hand, he could not manage his colostomy. We have never faced having to rehabilitate people with such extensive wounds. We are only beginning to learn what to do to make a life worth living possible for them.

* * * * *

On April 4, 2004, after four private military contractors were killed and their bodies mutilated in Fallujah, just to the west of Baghdad, three marine battalions launched an attack to take control of the city from the fifteen to twenty thousand insurgents operating there. Five days later, after intense fighting and protests from Iraqi authorities, the White House ordered the troops to retreat. The marines staged a second attack seven months afterward, on November 9. Four marine battalions and two army mechanized infantry battalions with some twelve thousand troops in all fought street-to-street against snipers and groups of insurgents hiding among the two hundred mosques and fifty thousand buildings of the city. The city was recaptured in about a week, although fighting continued for weeks afterward. During the two battles for Fallujah, American forces suffered more than 1,100 casualties in all, the insurgents a still-untold number. To care for the wounded, fewer than twenty trauma surgeons were in the vicinity; just two neurosurgeons were available in the entire country. Marine and army forward surgical teams received some of the wounded but were quickly overwhelmed. Others were transported by two-hundred-mile-per-hour Blackhawk medevac helicopters directly to combat support hospitals, about half of them to the 31st CSH in Baghdad.

Another of the surgeons I had trained with in Boston, Michael Murphy, was a reservist on duty there at the time. A North Carolina vascular surgeon, he had signed up with the army reserves in June 2004. In October, he got a call from central command. "I left Durham on a Sunday, and a week later I was in a convoy going down the Irish Road in Iraq with an M9 pistol in my hand, wondering what I had gotten myself into," he later told me.

The moment he arrived at the 31st CSH—he still had his bags in his hands—Murphy was sent to the operating room to help with a soldier who had shrapnel injuries to the abdomen, both legs missing, and a spouting arterial injury in one arm. It was the worst injury Murphy had ever seen. The physicians, nurses, and medics took him in like a wet pup. They worked together as more of a team than he'd ever experienced. "In two weeks, I went from a guy who was scared to death about whether I was going to cut it to the point where I was the most comfortable I had ever felt as a surgeon," he says.

With Operation Phantom Fury, as the military called the November battle for Fallujah, the CSH was strained almost to the breaking point. "The wounded came in waves of five, ten, fifteen every two hours," Murphy says. The CSH had twenty-five beds in the ER, five operating tables, and one critical care team, and that did not seem nearly enough. But they made do. Surgeons and emergency physicians saw the worst casualties as they came in. Family physicians, pediatricians, and even ophthalmologists—whoever was available—stabilized the less seriously injured. The surgical teams up in the operating rooms stuck to damage control surgery to keep the soldiers moving off the operating tables. Once stabilized, the American wounded were evacuated to Landstuhl. One-third of the patients were Iraqi wounded, and they had to stay until beds in Iraqi hospitals were found, if they were civilians or security forces, or until they were recovered enough to go to prison facilities, if they were insurgents. In the thick of it, Murphy says, he and his colleagues worked for forty-eight hours with little more than half-hour breaks here and there, grabbed some sleep, then worked for forty-eight hours more.

Six hundred and nine American soldiers were wounded in the first six days of the November battle. Nonetheless, the military teams managed to keep the overall death rate at just 10 percent. Of 1,100 American soldiers wounded during the twin battles for Fallujah, the teams saved all but 104—a stunning accomplishment. And it was only possible through a kind of resolute diligence that is difficult to imagine. Think, for example, about the fact that we even know the statistics of what happened to the wounded in Fallujah. It is only because the medical team took the time, despite the chaos and their fatigue, to fill our their logs describing the injuries and their outcomes. At the 31st CSH, three senior physicians took charge of collecting the data; they input more than seventy-five different pieces of information on every casualty—all so they could later analyze the patterns in what had happened to the soldiers and how effective the treatments had been. "We had a little doctors' room with two computers," Murphy recalls. "I remember I'd see those guys late at night, sometimes in the early hours of the morning, putting the data in."

We do little tracking like this here at home. Ask a typical American hospital what its death and complications rates for surgery were during the last six months and it cannot tell you. Few institutions ask their doctors to collect this information. Doctors don't have time, I am tempted to say. But then I remember those surgeons in Baghdad in the dark hours at their PCs. Knowing their results was so important to them that they skipped sleep to gather the data. They understood that such vigilance over the details of their own performance—the same kind of vigilance practiced by WHO physicians working to eradicate polio from the world and the Pittsburgh VA hospital units seeking to eliminate hospital infections—offered the only chance to do better.

* * * * *

As the war continued, medical teams were forced to confront numerous unanticipated circumstances. The war went on far longer than planned, the volume of wounded soldiers increased, and the nature of the injuries changed. The data, however, proved to be of crucial importance. Surgeons following the trauma logs began to see, for example, a dismayingly high incidence of blinding injuries. Soldiers had been directed to wear eye protection, but they evidently found the issued goggles too ugly. As one soldier put it, "They look like something a Florida senior citizen would wear." So the military bowed to fashion and switched to cooler-looking Wiley-brand ballistic eyewear. The rate of eye injuries decreased markedly.

Military doctors also found that blast injuries from suicide bombs, land mines, and other IEDs were increasing and were proving particularly difficult to manage. IEDs often produce a combination of penetrating, blunt, and burn injuries. The shrapnel include not only nails, bolts, and the like but also dirt, clothing, even bone from assailants. Victims of IED attacks can exsanguinate from multiple seemingly small wounds. The military therefore updated first aid kits to include emergency bandages that go on like a tourniquet over a wound and can be cinched down with one hand by the soldiers themselves. A newer bandage impregnated with a material that can clot blood more quickly was distributed. The surgical teams that receive blast injury victims learned to pack all the bleeding sites with gauze before starting abdominal surgery or other interventions. And they began to routinely perform serial operative washouts of wounds to ensure adequate removal of infectious debris.

This is not to say military physicians always found solutions. The logs have revealed many problems for which they do not yet have good answers. Early in the war in Iraq, for example, Kevlar vests proved dramatically effective in preventing torso injuries. Surgeons, however, found that IEDs were causing blast injuries that extend upward under the armor and inward through underarm vents. Blast injuries also produced an unprecedented number of what orthopedists term "mangled extremities"—limbs with severe soft-tissue, bone, and often vascular injuries. These can be devastating, potentially mortal injuries, and whether to amputate is one of the most difficult decisions in orthopedic surgery. Military surgeons used to rely on civilian trauma criteria to guide their choices. Examination of their outcomes, however, revealed that those criteria were not reliable in this war. Possibly because the limb injuries were more extreme or more often combined with injuries to other organs, attempts to salvage limbs by following the criteria frequently failed, resulting in life-threatening blood loss, gangrene, and sepsis.

Late complications emerged as a substantial difficulty, as well. Surgeons began to see startling rates of pulmonary embolism and lower-extremity blood clots (deep venous thrombosis), for example, perhaps because of the severity of the extremity injuries and reliance on long-distance transportation of the wounded. Initial data showed that 5 percent of the wounded arriving at Walter Reed developed pulmonary emboli, resulting in two deaths. There was no obvious solution. Using anticoagulants—blood thinners—in patients with fresh wounds and in need of multiple procedures seemed unwise.

Mysteriously, injured soldiers from Iraq also brought an epidemic of infections from a multidrug-resistant bacteria called *Acinetobacter baumanii.* No such epidemic appeared among soldiers from Afghanistan, and whether the drug resistance was produced by antibiotic use or was already carried in the strains that had colonized troops in Iraq is unknown. Regardless, data from 442 medical evacuees seen at Walter Reed in 2004 showed that thirty-seven (8.4 percent) were culture-positive for *acinetobacter*—a rate far higher than any previously experienced. The organism infected wounds, prostheses, and catheters in soldiers and spread to at least three other hospital patients. Later, medical evacuees from Iraq were routinely isolated on arrival and screened for the bacteria. Walter Reed, too, had to launch an effort to get health care personnel to be better about washing hands.

These were just the medical challenges. Other, equally pressing difficulties arose from the changing conditions of war. As the war converted from lightening-quick, highly mobile military operations to a more protracted, garrison effort, the CSHs had to adapt by converting to fixed facilities. In Baghdad, for example, medical personnel moved into the Ibn Sina hospital in the Green Zone. This shift brought increasing numbers of Iraqi civilians seeking care, and there was no overall policy about providing it. Some hospitals refused to treat civilians for fear of suicide bombers hiding among them in order to reach an American target. Others treated Iraqis but found themselves overwhelmed, particularly by pediatric patients, for whom they had limited personnel and few supplies.

Requests were made for additional staff members and resources at all levels. As the medical needs facing the military increased, however, the supply of medical personnel got tighter. Interest in signing up for military duty dropped precipitously. In 2004, according to the army, only fourteen other surgeons besides Murphy joined the reserves. Many surgeons were put on a second or extended deployment. But the numbers were not sufficient. Military urologists, plastic surgeons, and cardiothoracic surgeons were then tasked to fill some general surgeon positions. Planners began to contemplate ordering surgeons to take yet a third deployment. The Department of Defense announced that it would rely on improved financial incentives to attract more medical professionals. But the strategy did not succeed. The pay had never been competitive, and joined with the near certainty of leaving one's family for duty overseas and the dangerous nature of the work, it was not enough to encourage interest in entering military service. By the middle of 2005, the wars in Iraq and Afghanistan had stretched longer than American involvement in World War II—or in any war without a draft. In the absence of a draft, it has been extremely difficult for the nation's military surgical teams to maintain their remarkable performance.

Nonetheless, they have, at least thus far. At the end of 2006, medical teams were still saving an unbelievable 90 percent of soldiers wounded in battle. Military doctors continued to transform their strategies for the treatment of war casualties. They did so through a commitment to making a science of performance, rather than waiting for new discoveries. And they did it under extraordinarily demanding conditions and with heroic personal sacrifices.

One surgeon deserves particular recognition. Mark Taylor began his Army service in 2001 as general surgeon at Fort Bragg's Womack Army Medical Center, in North Carolina, to fulfill the terms of the military scholarship that had allowed him to attend George Washington University Medical School several years before. He, like many others, was twice deployed to Iraq—first from February through May 2003 and then from August 2003 through winter the next year, as a member of the 782nd Forward Surgical Team. On March 20, 2004, outside Fallujah, four days from returning home, the forty-one-year-old surgeon was hit in a rocket-propelled-grenade attack while trying to make a phone call outside his barracks. Despite his team's efforts, he could not be revived. No doctor has paid a greater price.

THE WAY WE AGE NOW

ATUL GAWANDE

The hardest substance in the human body is the white enamel of the teeth. With age, it wears away nonetheless, allowing the softer, darker layers underneath to show through. Meanwhile, the blood supply to the pulp and the roots of the teeth atrophies, and the flow of saliva diminishes; the gums tend to become inflamed and pull away from the teeth, exposing the base, making them unstable and elongating their appearance, especially the lower ones. Experts say they can gauge a person's age to within five years from the examination of a single tooth—if the person has any teeth left to examine.

Scrupulous dental care can help avert tooth loss, but growing old gets in the way. Arthritis, tremors, and small strokes, for example, make it difficult to brush and floss, and, because nerves become less sensitive with age, people may not realize that they have cavity and gum problems until it's too late. In the course of a normal lifetime, the muscles of the jaw lose about forty per cent of their mass and the bones of the mandible lose about twenty per cent, becoming porous and weak. The ability to chew declines, and people shift to softer foods, which are generally higher in fermentable carbohydrates and more likely to cause cavities. By the age of sixty, Americans have lost, on average, a third of their teeth. After eighty-five, almost forty per cent have no teeth at all.

Even as our bones and teeth soften, the rest of our body hardens. Blood vessels, joints, the muscle and valves of the heart, and even the lungs pick up substantial deposits of calcium and turn stiff. Under a microscope, the vessels and soft tissues display the same form of calcium that you find in bone. When you reach inside an elderly patient during surgery, the aorta and other major vessels often feel crunchy under your fingers. A recent study has found that loss of bone density may be an even better predictor of death from atherosclerotic disease than cholesterol levels. As we age, it's as if the calcium flows out of our skeletons and into our tissues.

To maintain the same volume of blood flow through narrowed and stiffened blood vessels, the heart has to generate increased pressure. As a result, more than half of us develop hypertension by the age of sixty-five. The heart becomes thicker-walled from having to pump against the pressure, and less able to respond to the demands of exertion. The peak output of the heart decreases steadily from the age of thirty. People become gradually less able to run as far or as fast as they used to, or to climb a flight of stairs without becoming short of breath.

* * * * *

Why we age is the subject of vigorous debate. The classical view is that aging happens because of random wear and tear. A newer view holds that aging is more orderly and genetically driven. Proponents of this view point out that animals of similar species and exposure to wear and tear have markedly different life spans. The Canada goose has a longevity of 23.5 years; the emperor goose only 6.3 years. Perhaps animals are like plants, with lives that are, to a large extent, internally governed. Certain species of bamboo, for instance, form a dense stand that grows and flourishes for a hundred years, flowers all at once, and then dies.

The idea that living things shut down and not just wear down has received substantial support in the past decade. Researchers working with the now famous worm *C. elegans* (two of the last five Nobel Prizes in medicine went to scientists doing work on the little nematode) were able to produce worms that live more than twice as long and age more slowly by altering a single gene. Scientists have since come up with single-gene alterations that increase the life spans of *Drosophila* fruit flies, mice, and yeast.

These findings notwithstanding, scientists do not believe that our life spans are actually programmed into us. After all, for most of our hundred-thousand-year existence—all but the past couple of hundred years—the average life span of human beings has been thirty years or less. (Research suggests that subjects of the Roman Empire had an average life expectancy of twenty-eight years.) Today, the average life span in developed countries is almost eighty years. If human life spans depend on our genetics, then medicine has got the upper hand. We are, in a way, freaks living well beyond our appointed time. So when we study aging what we are trying to understand is not so much a natural process as an unnatural one. Inheritance has surprisingly little influence on longevity. James Vaupel, of the Max Planck Institute for Demographic Research, in Rostock, Germany, notes that only six per cent of how long you'll live, compared with the average, is explained by your parents' longevity; by contrast, up to ninety per cent of how tall you are, compared with the average, is explained by your parents' height. Even genetically identical twins vary widely in life span: the typical gap is more than fifteen years.

If our genes explain less than we imagined, the wear-and-tear model may explain more than we knew. Leonid Gavrilov, a researcher at the University of Chicago, argues that human beings fail the way all complex systems fail: randomly and gradually. As engineers have long recognized, many simple devices do not age. They function reliably until a critical component fails, and the whole thing dies instantly. A windup toy works smoothly until a gear rusts or a spring breaks, and then it doesn't work at all. But complex systems—power plants, say—have to survive and function despite having thousands of critical components. Engineers therefore design these machines with multiple layers of redundancy: with backup systems, and backup systems for the backup systems. The backups may not be as efficient as the first-line components, but they allow the machine to keep going even as damage accumulates. Gavrilov argues that, within the parameters established by our genes, that's exactly how human beings appear to work. We have an extra kidney, an extra lung, an extra gonad, extra teeth. The DNA in our cells is frequently damaged under routine conditions, but our cells have a number of DNA repair systems. If a key gene is permanently damaged, there are usually extra copies of the gene nearby. And, if the entire cell dies, other cells can fill in.

Nonetheless, as the defects in a complex system increase, the time comes when just one more defect is enough to impair the whole, resulting in the condition known as frailty. It happens to power plants, cars, and large organizations. And it happens to us: eventually, one too many joints are damaged, one too many arteries calcify. There are no more backups. We wear down until we can't wear down anymore.

It happens in a bewildering array of ways. Hair grows gray, for instance, simply because we run out of the pigment cells that give hair its color. The natural life cycle of the scalp's pigment cells is just a few years. We rely on stem cells under the surface to migrate in and replace them. Gradually, however, the stem-cell reservoir is used up. By the age of fifty, as a result, half of the average person's hairs have gone gray.

Inside skin cells, the mechanisms that clear out waste products slowly break down and the muck coalesces into a clot of gooey yellow-brown pigment known as lipofuscin. These are the age spots we see in skin. When lipofuscin accumulates in sweat glands, the sweat glands cannot function, which helps explain why we become so susceptible to heat stroke and heat exhaustion in old age.

The eyes go for different reasons. The lens is made of crystallin proteins that are tremendously durable, but they change chemically in ways that diminish their elasticity over time—hence the farsightedness that most people develop beginning in their fourth decade. The process also gradually yellows the lens. Even without cataracts (the whitish clouding of the lens caused by excessive ultraviolet exposure, high cholesterol, diabetes, cigarette smoking, and other unhelpful conditions), the amount of light reaching the retina of a healthy sixty-year-old is one-third that of a twenty-year-old.

I spoke to Felix Silverstone, who for twenty-four years was the senior geriatrician at the Parker Jewish Institute, in New York, and has published more than a hundred studies on aging. There is, he said, "no single, common cellular mechanism to the aging process." Our bodies accumulate lipofuscin and oxygen free-radical damage and random DNA mutations and numerous other microcellular problems. The process is gradual and unrelenting. "We just fall apart," he said.

* * * * *

This is not an appealing prospect, and people naturally prefer to avoid the subject of their decrepitude. There have been dozens of best-selling books on aging, but they tend to have titles like "Younger Next Year," "The Fountain of Age," "Ageless," "The Sexy Years." Still, there are costs to averting our eyes from the realities. For one thing, we put off changes that we need to make as a society. For another, we deprive ourselves of opportunities to change the individual experience of aging for the better.

For nearly all of human existence, people died young. Life expectancy improved as we overcame early death—in particular, deaths from childbirth, infection, and traumatic injury. By the nineteen-seventies, just four out of every hundred people born in industrialized countries died before the age of thirty. It was an extraordinary achievement, but one that seemed to leave little room for further gain; even *eliminating* deaths before thirty would not raise over-all life expectancy significantly. Efforts shifted, therefore, to reducing deaths during middle and old age, and, in the decades since, the average life span has continued upward. Improvements in the treatment and prevention of heart disease, respiratory illness, stroke, cancer, and the like mean that the average sixty-five-year-old can expect to live another nineteen years—almost four years longer than was the case in 1970. (By contrast, from the nineteenth century to 1970, sixty-five-year-olds gained just three years of life expectancy.)

The result has been called the "rectangularization" of survival. Throughout most of human history, a society's population formed a sort of pyramid: young children represented the largest portion—the base—and each successively older cohort represented a smaller and smaller group. In 1950, children under the age of five were eleven per cent of the U.S. population, adults aged forty-five to forty-nine were six per cent, and those over eighty were one per cent. Today, we have as many fifty-year-olds as five-year-olds. In thirty years, there will be as many people over eighty as there are under five.

Americans haven't come to grips with the new demography. We cling to the notion of retirement at sixty-five—a reasonable notion when those over sixty-five were a tiny percentage of the population, but completely untenable as they approach twenty per cent. People are putting aside less in savings for old age now than they have in any decade since the Great Depression. More than half of the very old now live without a spouse, and we have fewer children than ever before—yet we give virtually no thought to how we will live out our later years alone.

Equally worrying, and far less recognized, medicine has been slow to confront the very changes that it has been responsible for—or to apply the knowledge we already have about how to make old age better. Despite a rapidly growing elderly population, the number of certified geriatricians fell by a third between 1998 and 2004. Applications to training programs in adult primary-care medicine are plummeting, while fields like plastic surgery and radiology receive applications in record numbers. Partly, this has to do with money—incomes in geriatrics and adult primary care are among the lowest in medicine. And partly, whether we admit it or not, most doctors don't like taking care of the elderly.

"Mainstream doctors are turned off by geriatrics, and that's because they do not have the faculties to cope with the Old Crock," Felix Silverstone, the geriatrician, explained to me. "The Old Crock is deaf. The Old Crock has poor vision. The Old Crock's memory might be somewhat impaired. With the Old Crock, you have to slow down, because he asks you to repeat what you are saying or asking. And the Old Crock doesn't just have a chief complaint—the Old Crock has fifteen chief complaints. How in the world are you going to cope with all of them? You're overwhelmed. Besides, he's had a number of these things for fifty years or so. You're not going to cure something he's had for fifty years. He has high blood pressure. He has diabetes. He has arthritis. There's nothing glamorous about taking care of any of those things."

There is, however, a skill to it, a developed body of professional expertise. And until I visited my hospital's geriatrics clinic and saw the work that geriatricians do, I did not fully grasp the nature of that expertise, or how important it could be for all of us.

* * * * *

The geriatrics clinic—or, as my hospital calls it, the Center for Older Adult Health—is only one floor below my surgery clinic. I pass by it almost every day, and I can't remember ever giving it a moment's thought. One morning, however, I wandered downstairs and, with the permission of the patients, sat in on a few visits with Juergen Bludau, the chief geriatrician.

"What brings you here today?" the doctor asked Jean Gavrilles, his first patient of the morning. She was eighty-five years old, with short, frizzy white hair, oval glasses, a lavender knit shirt, and a sweet, ready smile. Small but sturdy in appearance, she had come in walking steadily, her purse and coat clutched under one arm, her daughter trailing behind her, no support required beyond her mauve orthopedic shoes. She said that her internist had recommended that she come.

About anything in particular? the doctor asked.

The answer, it seemed, was yes and no. The first thing she mentioned was a lower-back pain that she'd had for months, which shot down her leg and sometimes made it difficult to get out of bed or up from a chair. She also had bad arthritis, and she showed us her fingers, which were swollen at the knuckles and bent out to the sides with what's called a swan-neck deformity. She'd had both knees replaced a decade earlier. She had high blood pressure "from stress," she said, and handed him her list of medications. She had glaucoma and needed to have eye exams every four months. She never used to have "bathroom problems," but lately, she admitted, she'd started wearing a pad. She'd also had surgery for colon cancer and, by the way, now had a lung nodule that the radiology report said could be a metastasis—a biopsy was recommended.

Bludau asked her to tell him about her life. She said that she lived alone, except for her Yorkshire terrier, in a single-family house in the West Roxbury section of Boston. Her husband died of lung cancer twenty-three years ago. She did not drive. She had a son living in the area who did her shopping once a week and checked on her each day—"just to see if I'm still alive," she joked. Another son and two daughters lived farther away, but they helped as well. Otherwise, she took care of herself quite capably. She did her own cooking and cleaning. She managed her medicines and her bills. "I have a system," she said. She had a high-school education, and during the war she'd worked as a riveter at the Charlestown Navy Yard. She also worked for a time at the Jordan Marsh department store in downtown Boston. But that was a long time ago. She stuck to home now, with her yard and her terrier and her family when they visited.

The doctor asked her about her day in great detail. She usually woke around five or six o'clock, she said—she didn't seem to need much sleep anymore. She would get out of bed as the back pain allowed, take a shower, and get dressed. Downstairs, she'd take her medicines, feed the dog, and eat breakfast. Bludau asked what she had for breakfast. Cereal and a banana. She hated bananas, she said, but she'd heard they were good for her potassium, so she was afraid to stop. After breakfast, she'd take her dog for a little walk in the yard. She did chores—laundry, cleaning, and the like. In the late morning, she took a break to watch "The Price Is Right." At lunchtime, she had a sandwich and orange juice. If the weather was nice, she'd sit out in the yard afterward. She'd loved working in her garden, but she couldn't do that anymore. The afternoons were slow. She might do some more chores. She might nap or talk on the phone. Eventually, she would make dinner—a salad and maybe a baked potato or a scrambled egg. At night, she watched the Red Sox or the Patriots or college basketball—she loved sports. She usually went to bed at about midnight.

Bludau asked her to sit on the examining table. As she struggled to climb up, her balance teetering on the step, the doctor held her arm. He checked her blood pressure, which was normal. He examined her eyes and ears and had her open her mouth. He listened to her heart and lungs briskly, through his stethoscope. He began to slow down only when he looked at her hands. The nails were neatly trimmed.

"Who cuts your nails?" he asked.

"I do," Gavrilles replied.

I tried to think what could be accomplished in this visit. She was in good condition for her age, but she faced everything from advancing arthritis and incontinence to what might be metastatic colon cancer. It seemed to me that, with just a forty-minute visit, Bludau needed to triage by zeroing in on either the most potentially life-threatening problem (the possible metastasis) or the problem that bothered her the most (the back pain). But this was evidently not what he thought. He asked almost nothing about either issue. Instead, he spent much of the exam looking at her feet.

"Is that really necessary?" she asked, when he instructed her to take off her shoes and socks.

"Yes," he said. After she'd left, he told me, "You must always examine the feet." He described a bow-tied gentleman who seemed dapper and fit, until his feet revealed the truth: he couldn't bend down to reach them, and they turned out not to have been cleaned in weeks, suggesting neglect and real danger.

Gavrilles had difficulty taking her shoes off, and, after watching her struggle a bit, Bludau leaned in to help. When he got her socks off, he took her feet in his hands, one at a time. He inspected them inch by inch—the soles, the toes, the web spaces. Then he helped her get her socks and shoes back on and gave her and her daughter his assessment.

She was doing impressively well, he said. She was mentally sharp and physically strong. The danger for her was losing what she had. The single most serious threat she faced was not the lung nodule or the back pain. It was falling. Each year, about three hundred and fifty thousand Americans fall and break a hip. Of those, forty per cent end up in a nursing home, and twenty per cent are never able to walk again. The three primary risk factors for falling are poor balance, taking more than four prescription medications, and muscle weakness. Elderly people without these risk factors have a twelve-per-cent chance of falling in a year. Those with all three risk factors have almost a hundred-per-cent chance. Jean Gavrilles had at least two. Her balance was poor. Though she didn't need a walker, he had noticed her splay-footed gait as she came in. Her feet were swollen. The toenails were unclipped. There were sores between the toes. And the balls of her feet had thick, rounded calluses.

She was also on five medications. Each was undoubtedly useful, but, together, the usual side effects would include dizziness. In addition, one of the blood-pressure medications was a diuretic, and she seemed to drink few liquids, risking dehydration and a worsening of the dizziness. Her tongue was bone dry when Bludau examined it.

She did not have significant muscle weakness, and that was good. When she got out of her chair, he said, he noted that she had not used her arms to push herself up. She simply stood up—a sign of well-preserved muscle strength. From the details of the day she described, however, she did not seem to be eating nearly enough calories to maintain that strength. Bludau asked her whether her weight had changed recently. She admitted that she had lost about seven pounds in the previous six months.

The job of any doctor, Bludau later told me, is to support quality of life, by which he meant two things: as much freedom from the ravages of disease as possible, and the retention of enough function for active engagement in the world. Most doctors treat disease, and figure that the rest will take care of itself. And if it doesn't—if a patient is becoming infirm and heading toward a nursing home—well, that isn't really a *medical* problem, is it?

To a geriatrician, though, it *is* a medical problem. People can't stop the aging of their bodies and minds, but there are ways to make it more manageable, and to avert at least some of the worst effects. So Bludau referred Gavrilles to a podiatrist, whom he wanted her to visit once every four weeks, for better care of her feet. He didn't see medications that he could eliminate, but he switched her diuretic to a blood-pressure medicine that wouldn't cause dehydration. He recommended that she eat a snack during the day, get all the low-calorie and low-cholesterol food out of the house, and see whether family or friends could join her for more meals. "Eating alone is not very stimulating," he said. And he asked her to see him again in three months, so that he could make sure the plan was working.

Nine months later, I checked in with Gavrilles and her daughter. She turned eighty-six this past November. She is eating better, and has even gained a pound or two. She still lives comfortably and independently in her own home. And she has not had a single fall.

* * * * *

In the story of Jean Gavrilles and her geriatrician, there's a lesson about frailty. Decline remains our fate; death will come. But, until that last backup system inside each of us fails, decline can occur in two ways. One is early and precipitately, with an old age of enfeeblement and dependence, sustained primarily by nursing homes and hospitals. The other way is more gradual, preserving, for as long as possible, your ability to control your own life.

Good medical care can influence which direction a person's old age will take. Most of us in medicine, however, don't know how to think about decline. We're good at addressing specific, individual problems: colon cancer, high blood pressure, arthritic knees. Give us a disease, and we can do something about it. But give us an elderly woman with colon cancer, high blood pressure, arthritic knees, and various other ailments besides—an elderly woman at risk of losing the life she enjoys—and we are not sure what to do.

Several years ago, researchers in St. Paul, Minnesota, identified five hundred and sixty-eight men and women over the age of seventy who were living independently but were at high risk of becoming disabled because of chronic health problems, recent illness, or cognitive changes. With their permission, the researchers randomly assigned half of them to see a team of geriatric specialists. The others were asked to see their usual physician, who was notified of their high-risk status. Within eighteen months, ten per cent of the patients in both groups had died. But the patients who had seen a geriatrics team were a third less likely to become disabled and half as likely to develop depression. They were forty per cent less likely to require home health services.

Little of what the geriatricians had done was high-tech medicine: they didn't do lung biopsies or back surgery or PET scans. Instead, they simplified medications.

They saw that arthritis was controlled. They made sure toenails were trimmed and meals were square. They looked for worrisome signs of isolation and had a social worker check that the patient's home was safe.

How do we reward this kind of work? Chad Boult, who was the lead investigator of the St. Paul study and a geriatrician at the University of Minnesota, can tell you. A few months after he published his study, demonstrating how much better people's lives were with specialized geriatric care, the university closed the division of geriatrics.

"The university said that it simply could not sustain the financial losses," Boult said from Baltimore, where he is now a professor at the Johns Hopkins Bloomberg School of Public Health. On average, in Boult's study, the geriatric services cost the hospital $1,350 more per person than the savings they produced, and Medicare, the insurer for the elderly, does not cover that cost. It's a strange double standard. No one insists that a twenty-five-thousand-dollar pacemaker or a coronary-artery stent save money for insurers. It just has to *maybe* do people some good. Meanwhile, the twenty-plus members of the proven geriatrics team at the University of Minnesota had to find new jobs. Scores of medical centers across the country have shrunk or closed their geriatrics units. Several of Boult's colleagues no longer advertise their geriatric training for fear that they'll get too many elderly patients. "Economically, it has become too difficult," Boult said.

But the finances are only a symptom of a deeper reality: people have not insisted on a change in priorities. We all like new medical gizmos and demand that policymakers make sure they are paid for. They feed our hope that the troubles of the body can be fixed for good. But geriatricians? Who clamors for geriatricians? What geriatricians do—bolster our resilience in old age, our capacity to weather what comes—is both difficult and unappealingly limited. It requires attention to the body and its alterations. It requires vigilance over nutrition, medications, and living situations. And it requires each of us to contemplate the course of our decline, in order to make the small changes that can reshape it. When the prevailing fantasy is that we can be ageless, the geriatrician's uncomfortable demand is that we accept we are not.

* * * * *

For Felix Silverstone, understanding human aging has been the work of a lifetime. He was a national leader in geriatrics for five decades. But he is now himself eighty-seven years old. He can feel his own mind and body wearing down, and much of what he spent his career studying is no longer abstract to him.

Felix has been fortunate. He didn't have to stop working, even after he suffered a heart attack in his sixties which cost him half his heart function; nor was he stopped by a near-cardiac arrest at the age of seventy-nine. "One evening, sitting at home, I suddenly became aware of palpitations," he told me. "I was just reading, and a few minutes later I became short of breath. A little bit after that, I began to feel heavy in the chest. I took my pulse, and it was over two hundred." He is the sort of person who, in the midst of chest pain, would take the opportunity to examine his own pulse. "My wife and I had a little discussion about whether or not to call an ambulance. We decided to call."

When Felix got to the hospital, the doctors had to shock him to bring his heart back. He'd had ventricular fibrillation, and an automatic defibrillator had to be installed in his chest. Within a few weeks, though, he felt well again, and his doctor cleared him to return to work full time. He stayed in medical practice after the attack, multiple hernia repairs, gallbladder surgery, arthritis that ended his avid piano playing, compression fractures of his aging spine that stole three full inches of his once five-foot-seven-inch height, and hearing loss. "I switched to an electronic stethoscope," he said. "They're a nuisance, but they're very good."

Finally, at eighty-two, he had to retire. The problem wasn't his health; it was that of his wife, Bella. They'd been married for more than sixty years. Felix had met Bella when he was an intern and she was a dietitian at Kings County Hospital, in Brooklyn. They brought up two sons in Flatbush. When the boys left home, Bella got her teaching certification and began working with children who had learning disabilities. In her seventies, however, retinal disease diminished her vision, and she had to stop working. A decade later, she became almost completely blind. Felix no longer felt safe leaving her at home alone, and in 2001 he gave up his practice. They moved to Orchard Cove, a retirement community in Canton, Massachusetts, outside Boston, where they could be closer to their sons.

"I didn't think I would survive the change," Felix said. He'd observed in his patients how difficult the transitions of age could be. Examining his last patient, packing up his home, he felt that he was about to die. "I was taking apart my life as well as the house," he recalled. "It was terrible."

We were sitting in a library off Orchard Cove's main lobby. There was light streaming through a picture window, tasteful art on the walls, white-upholstered Federal-style armchairs. It was like a nice hotel, only with no one under seventy-five walking around. Felix and Bella have a two-bedroom apartment with forest views and plenty of space. In the living room, he has his grand piano and, at his desk, piles of medical journals that he still subscribes to—"for my soul," he said. Theirs is an independent-living unit. It comes with housekeeping, linen changes, and dinner each evening. When they need to, they can upgrade to assisted living, which provides three prepared meals and up to an hour with a personal-care assistant each day.

This was not the average retirement community, but even in an average one rent runs thirty-two thousand dollars a year. Entry fees are typically sixty thousand to a hundred and twenty thousand dollars on top of that. Meanwhile, the median income of people eighty and older is only about fifteen thousand dollars. More than half of the elderly who live in long-term-care facilities go through their entire savings and have to go on Medicaid—welfare—in order to afford it. And, ultimately, the average American spends a year or more of his old age disabled and living in a nursing home (at twice the cost), which is a destination Felix desperately hopes to avoid.

He tries to note the changes he's experiencing objectively, like a good geriatrician. He notices that his skin has dried out. His sense of smell has diminished. His night vision has become poor. He tires easily. He has begun to lose teeth. He takes measures where he can. He uses lotion to avoid skin cracks; he protects himself from the heat; he gets on an exercise bike three times a week; he sees a dentist twice a year.

He's most concerned about the changes in his brain. "I can't think as clearly as I used to," he said. "I used to be able to read the *Times* in half an hour. Now it takes me an hour and a half." Even then, he's not sure that he has understood as much as he did before, and his memory gives him trouble. "If I go back and look at what I've read, I recognize that I went through it, but sometimes I don't really remember it," he said. "It's a matter of short-term registration. It's hard to get the signal in and have it stay put."

He makes use of methods that he once taught his patients. "I try to deliberately focus on what I'm doing, rather than do it automatically," he told me. "I haven't lost the automaticity of action, but I can't rely on it the way I used to. For example, I can't think about something else and get dressed and be sure I've gotten all the way dressed." He recognizes that the strategy doesn't always work. He sometimes told me the same story twice in a conversation. The lines of thought in his mind would fall into well-worn grooves and, however hard he tried to put them onto a new path, sometimes they resisted. Felix's knowledge as a geriatrician has forced him to recognize his own decline, but that hasn't made it easier to accept.

"I get blue occasionally," he said. "I think I have recurring episodes of depression. They are not enough to disable me, but they are..." He paused to find the right word. "They are uncomfortable."

What buoys him, despite his limitations, is having a purpose. It's the same purpose, he says, that sustained him in medicine: to be of service, in some way, to those around him. He had been in Orchard Cove for only a few months before he was helping to steer a committee to improve the health-care services there. He tried to form a journal-reading club for retired physicians. He even guided a young geriatrician through her first independent-research study—a survey of the residents' attitudes toward Do Not Resuscitate orders.

More important is the responsibility that he feels for his children and grand-children—and, most of all, for Bella. Her blindness and recent memory troubles have made her deeply dependent. Without him, I suspect, she would probably be in a nursing home. He helps her dress. He administers her medicines. He makes her break-fast and lunch. He takes her on walks and to doctors' appointments. "She is my purpose now," he said. Bella doesn't always like his way of doing things. "We argue constantly—we're at each other about a lot of things," Felix said. "But we're also very forgiving."

He does not feel this responsibility to be a burden. With the narrowing of his own life, his ability to look after Bella has become his main source of self-worth. "I am exclusively her caregiver," he said. "I am glad to be." And this role has heightened his sense that he must be attentive to the changes in his own capabilities; he is no good to her if he isn't honest with himself about what he can and can't do.

One evening, Felix invited me to dinner. The formal dining hall was restaurant-like, with reserved seating, table service, and jackets required. I was wearing my white hospital coat and had to borrow a navy blazer from the maître d'. Felix, in a brown suit and a stone-colored oxford shirt, gave his arm to Bella, who wore a blue-flowered knee-length dress that he'd picked out for her, and guided her to the table. She was amiable and chatty and had youthful-seeming eyes. But, once she'd been seated, she couldn't find the plate in front of her, let alone the menu. Felix ordered for her: wild-rice soup, an omelette, mashed potatoes, and mashed cauliflower. "No salt," he instructed the waiter; she had high blood pressure. He ordered salmon and mashed potatoes for himself. I had the soup and a London broil.

When the food arrived, Felix told Bella where she could find the different items on her plate by the hands of a clock. He put a fork in her hand. Then he turned to his own meal.

Both made a point of chewing slowly. She was the first to choke. It was the omelette. Her eyes watered. She began to cough. Felix guided her water glass to her mouth. She took a drink and managed to get the omelette down.

"As you get older, the lordosis of your spine tips your head forward," he said to me. "So when you look straight ahead it's like looking up at the ceiling for anyone else. Try to swallow while looking up: you'll choke once in a while. The problem is common in the elderly. Listen." I realized that I could hear someone in the dining room choking on his food every minute or so. Felix turned to Bella. "You have to eat looking down, sweetie," he said.

A couple of bites later, though, he himself was choking. It was the salmon. He began coughing. He turned red. Finally, he was able to cough up the bite. It took a minute for him to catch his breath. "Didn't follow my own advice," he said.

Felix Silverstone is, without question, up against the debilities of his years. Once, it would have been remarkable simply to have lived to see eighty-seven. Now what's remarkable is that he has the control over his life that he does. When he started in geriatric practice, it was almost inconceivable that an eighty-seven-year-old with his history of health problems could live independently, care for his disabled wife, and continue to contribute to research. Even today, most people his age cannot live as he does.

Partly, he has been lucky. His memory, for example, has not deteriorated significantly. But he has also managed his old age well. His goal has been modest: to have as decent a life as medical knowledge and the limits of his body will allow. So he saved and did not retire early, and therefore is not in financial straits. He kept his social contacts, and avoided isolation. He monitored his bones and teeth and weight. And he has made sure to find a doctor who had the geriatric skills to help him hold on to an independent life.

* * * * *

I asked Chad Boult, the geriatrics professor now at Johns Hopkins, what can be done to insure that there are enough geriatricians for our country's surging elderly population. "Nothing," he said. "It's too late." Creating geriatricians takes years, and we already have far too few. This year, just three hundred doctors will complete geriatrics training, not nearly enough to replace the geriatricians going into retirement, let alone meet the needs of the next decade.

Yet Boult believes that we still have time for another strategy: he would direct geriatricians toward training all primary-care doctors in caring for the very old, instead of providing the care themselves. Even this is a tall order—ninety-seven per cent of medical students take no course in geriatrics, and the strategy requires that the nation pay geriatricians to teach rather than to provide patient care. But, if the will is there, Boult estimates that it would be possible to establish courses in every medical school and internal-medicine training program within a decade. "We've got to do something," he said. "Life for older people can be better than it is today."

Boult and his colleagues have yet another strategy, just in case—a strategy that they have called Guided Care, and that doesn't depend on doctors at all. They're recruiting local nurses for a highly compressed, three-week course in how to recognize specific problems in the elderly, such as depression, malnutrition, isolation, and danger of falling; how to formulate a plan to remedy those problems; and how to work with patients, families, and doctors to follow through on the plan. In a test of the strategy, the researchers are putting the nurses to work in primary-care practices around Baltimore and Washington, D.C., and studying the results. It is a meagre solution for a huge problem, but it is cheap, which insurers demand, and, if it provides even a fraction of the benefit geriatricians have, it could nudge medical care in the right direction.

* * * * *

"I can still drive, you know," Felix Silverstone said to me. "I'm a very good driver."

After our dinner together, he had to go on an errand to refill Bella's prescriptions in Stoughton, a few miles away, and I asked if I could go along. He had a gold 1998 Toyota Camry with automatic transmission and thirty-nine thousand miles on the odometer. It was pristine, inside and out. He backed out of a narrow parking space and zipped out of the garage. His hands did not shake. Taking the streets of Canton at dusk on a new-moon night, he brought the car to an even stop at the red lights, signalled when he was supposed to, took turns without a hitch.

I was, I admit, braced for disaster. The risk of a fatal car crash with a driver who's eighty-five or older is more than three times higher than it is with a driver between sixteen and twenty. The very old are the highest-risk drivers on the road. This past fall, in Los Angeles, George Weller was convicted of manslaughter after he confused the accelerator with the brake pedal and plowed his Buick into a crowd of shoppers at the Santa Monica Farmers' Market. Ten people were killed, and more than sixty were injured. He was eighty-six.

But Felix showed no difficulties. At one point during our drive, poorly marked road construction at an intersection channelled our line of cars almost directly into oncoming traffic. Felix corrected course swiftly, pulling over into the proper lane. There is no saying how much longer he will be able to count on his driving ability. The day may well come when he will have to give up his keys.

At the moment, though, he wasn't concerned; he was glad simply to be on the road. The evening traffic was thin as he turned onto Route 138. He brought the Camry to a tick over the forty-five-mile-per-hour speed limit. He had his window rolled down and his elbow on the sash. The air was clear and cool, and we listened to the sound of the wheels on the pavement.

"The night is lovely, isn't it?" he said.

THE MAN HE KILLED

THOMAS HARDY

Had he and I but met
By some old ancient inn,
We should have set us down to wet
Right many a nipperkin!

But ranged as infantry,
And staring face to face,
I shot at him as he at me,
And killed him in his place.

I shot him dead because—
Because he was my foe,
Just so: my foe of course he was;
That's clear enough; although

He thought he'd 'list, perhaps,
Off-hand like—just as I—
Was out of work—had sold his traps—
No other reason why.

Yes; quaint and curious war is!
You shoot a fellow down
You'd treat, if met where any bar is,
Or help to half a crown.

WINTHROP COHEN

ARTHUR KLEINMAN

I met him in a clinical consultation more than twenty-five years ago. More accurately, I first met Mrs. Julia Richardson Cohen and her married daughter, Alexandra Frost—both tall, attractive, conservatively dressed, and worried. Winthrop had, at the last minute, backed out of accompanying them.

"So what's the problem?" I asked mother and daughter.

"He won't talk about it," Mrs. Cohen told me. "Says he can't. But it is eating him up inside. I married a vibrant, wonderful man. Now he seems so sad, so hurt. It's not right. He's been so successful. We have everything anyone would want. So why does he seem so unhappy, so terribly unhappy?"

Mrs. Cohen's daughter added, "He's all closed up. We love him. He loves us. But we don't talk. Because he can't tell us what hurts so very much. But we're afraid, afraid for him." Then they both broke into sobs.

When they composed themselves, they told me they were quite sure Winthrop would come to see me, because he loved them and knew they were desperate for him to receive professional care. And indeed he did keep the next appointment several days later.

A short, stocky, immaculately attired, sixtyish man with a military bearing—straight back, shoulders squared, sitting bolt upright at the edge of his chair, hair in a brush cut, speech clipped, but otherwise expressionless—Winthrop Cohen made no effort to contradict his wife and daughter.

"They're probably right. I accept all the responsibility. It's my fault."

"What's your fault?"

"The way I am, I guess."

"What way is that?"

"Ah, what to say, huh? Where to start?"

He sighed—long, slow, and very deep. He looked down at the floor. His face fell into a desperate sadness that made him look greatly vulnerable. It was now clear why his wife and daughter were so worried. He seemed on the verge of collapsing. I waited. After what seemed like a two- or three-minute pause, he cleared his throat, bit his lip, and began.

"The war. It's what happened to me in the war. I could never get over it. But I learned to live with it. Then all of a sudden on my sixtieth birthday it became a terrible weight. I couldn't put it out of my mind. I feel so very depressed about it. Sometimes I sit for hours, brooding over the past. What I saw, what I did. My daughter calls it depression. I don't know what it is. But whatever it is, it is bad."

Winthrop Cohen had run away from home in a working-class section of lower Manhattan to join the Marines. The year was 1942. He was eighteen but looked older. After several months in training camp, he was shipped out to the Pacific theater. By the time the war ended, he had participated in the invasion of four islands including Okinawa, been twice decorated for bravery, and sustained two wounds, both visually impressive. One, a thin burn on the left side of his face, high across the cheekbone, extended from under his eye almost to his ear. It had turned lighter than the rest of his facial skin, which had a ruddy complexion, and had the effect of making him seem fierce and piratical, yet also aristocratic. The other, a long, deep, dark, dense scar on the outer surface of his right arm from wrist to elbow, a shrapnel wound, made me think of the kind of work injury a construction worker might fall prey to. Those two contrasting images—elite and blue-collar—created my sense of what Winthrop was about.

He was demobilized in 1945, after which he returned to New York, attended college on the GI Bill, received a scholarship to law school, and moved to the West Coast, where he joined a large law firm. Over the years he had been very successful and was now a senior partner. His wife came from the wealthy Protestant business class of this southern California city. Over four decades, the Cohens had one child, enjoyed a happy family life, and became well-to-do, respected members of the city's elite.

Winthrop Cohen was the son of an unsuccessful small businessman, a second-generation Jewish American who had gone from one failed business to another; his mother, a teacher and nonobservant Jew, had intentionally given him an aristocratic- and Protestant-sounding first name as a sign of her high aspirations for his success.* Winthrop's maternal grandfather, her father, had been successful as a builder of residential apartments, and Winthrop Cohen referred to himself as a "builder." "My father was a failure. He couldn't make a go of business, or family, or himself really. But I was like my grandfather. I was a builder, building a very successful career and a family. I'm proud of what I accomplished in *this* part of my life."

---

*To me his name, with its contrast of Protestant upper class and Jewish lower middle class, and the contrast of his scars, one of which, as I've noted, looks like a scar from an elite duel and the other like a workingman's injury, highlights the man's dividedness, which helps explain what he was about. Over the years I came to think of him by his full name, Winthrop Cohen, rather than just Winthrop. In this chapter I use his full name quite often in order to convey this sense.

About his three years in the Marines, Winthrop Cohen was less proud, and he had been silent for four decades at the time I met him. Neither to family nor friends nor for purposes of advancing his legal and business interests had he spoken of his wartime experience. He purposely avoided veterans' organizations and the alumni gatherings of his Marine unit. When an article appeared in a local newspaper in the 1950s listing winners of military decorations in the city, it carried Winthrop's name but neither his picture nor his story; he had refused to be interviewed. When sick a decade after the war with complications of the hepatitis he had been infected with in the service, he explicitly rejected the suggestion of going to the local veterans' hospital. "I did all I could to put it all behind me. I froze it out. Even memories, whenever they popped up, I pushed them away. Until now I was successful. I was aware of course that I had a hidden life, a part of me that discredited who I was, I mean had become, but I could control it, until now."

What so thoroughly shook Winthrop Cohen were the memories of beach landings, fighting in the jungle, and, most of all, killing. "I was made over into a killer. A proficient, remorseless killer. I probably killed dozens of enemy soldiers. Most at a distance, but several very close up. One, I bashed his head in with my rifle butt after he infiltrated our lines. He was a young kid. I guess my own age. I just kept hitting him in the face with that end of the rifle. I broke everything, his nose, his mouth, his eyes.

He had knifed the guy in the next hole. I heard the scream. I came running. The kid froze. I could have shot him. But I wanted to really hurt him, so I destroyed him blow after blow, till the rifle was covered in blood and gore. Then I sat down and retched. Another Jap (I hate the word now, but I used [it] plenty then)—a fat sergeant—was wounded in the gut. He had been part of a machine gun crew that tore our unit to pieces. I just shot him. But that wasn't enough. I was uncontrollable, in a rage. I took my bayonet and…well, better not say what I did, but it was bad. We mutilated them sometimes, and they did even worse things to our guys.

"But these two murders aren't the worst. You can understand them in a way and maybe even say things to justify them. But I did something, something so awful, there is—there can be no justification, no explanation, nothing to make it seem right. Nothing can exonerate me. This is the thing I have hidden all these years. The secret I have kept. The thing I did that can't, can never be undone.

"He must have been a military doctor. We overran his position. A small field hospital. There were guys on stretchers, almost dead. He raised his hands, dropping the stethoscope at his feet. He had been bent over this stretcher, treating a guy with a lot of blood on his chest. He raised his hands and looked at me. His eyes were fixed on me. He just watched me. I can see him—so quiet, just waiting. Thoughtful, sensitive. He didn't plead. He didn't say anything. He didn't move at all. He just looked at me. When I force myself to see it all over again, he seems so human, so sympathetic. His face was drawn and sad, waiting. Oh, God! I shot him. I killed him. He slid to the ground still looking at me. And I…I shot him again and again.

"At that point, let's face it, we weren't taking prisoners. But saying that is no good. I could have taken him prisoner. It was me, Winthrop Cohen, not we or they, who killed him. In cold blood. Without any threat. There is no other word for it. I murdered him. I murdered a doctor while he tended to his wounded men. Pure and simple. I killed an innocent man—no, I really think it is worse than that. I often think of that doctor. Who he was. What he did. What was he thinking? He waited, but he knew, he seemed to know what I would do. He didn't run or plead or fight. He just watched me. I mean, in my dreams he watches me. He waits. He accepts what I do.

"The more I think about him the more Christlike he becomes, from the sorrow in his eyes to the bullet wounds and blood. I murdered a healer, a man of deep humanity. I'm sure of that.

"How could I? How could I do that?" Winthrop Cohen wept. His voice became strangled. He made no effort now to control the flow of feeling, which swept over him in great sobs.

I reached out to touch his arm. "I hear you. I understand." But in fact I didn't and couldn't understand an experience that seemed to me as gruesome as anything I had heard. We both sat there in silence, stunned by the horrible remembrance; an image of the murdered Japanese doctor took over the room. There were no words to undo what Winthrop Cohen had done or to make up for what he had gone through.

"There is no end to it, you know. No way to close it out. I can't go back and change what happened. I want to. But I can never change what I did. I don't accept the usual.... It's war. Men do bad things, have to do awful things. Everything pure I believe in, I betrayed. I was raised to aspire to do the right things. My mother was a humanist. She taught me to love books. She made me feel that we Jews were different, special. Because we were bound to God, we were bound to doing good in the world. And look at me. I destroyed what I was raised to value. How can I face myself?

"When we were on the troopship waiting to board the landing craft, my first time, a lot of us were scared, and try as we did to hide it, it showed. We shivered, stuttered, vomited. Wet our pants. I knew I was scared. Then some fierce Marine major turned on us. He called us every name in the book, and then he bellowed, 'Most of you shits will die on this beach. Just be sure when you're hit, you goddam fall forward. So you don't get in the way of the guys behind you.' He meant it. His job was to take the beach and advance. You were nothing but his tools to do it. Expendable. That's what no one comprehends outside of battle. You killed and got killed. That's the way you were trained. To be tough as hell, hard, truly hard, and that means inhuman, cruelly inhuman.

"That's the other part of it. I was no aberration. I was normal, supernormal. A hero. The hero taught to kill, and along the way to betray every decent value of peacetime society. If you couldn't do it, you were mocked until you did, or thrown aside, so some other poor SOB could do it. I mock myself because I succeeded so well... because I can't turn back or turn it off."

Winthrop Cohen's remorse and regret were accompanied by almost all the cardinal symptoms of depression listed in the American Psychiatric Association's *Diagnostic and Statistical Manual* (which was in its third edition at the time): sadness, anhedonia (lack of pleasure), loss of sexual interest, sleep disturbance with early morning wakening, profound lack of energy, difficulty concentrating, agitation, appetite loss with a ten-pound weight loss, slowing down of all motor functions, and deep feelings of guilt, worthlessness, and hopelessness. As a young psychiatrist who had recently passed the clinical examination of the American Board of Neurology and Psychiatry, I knew that the appropriate treatment was to combine the right psychopharmacological drug with at least several months of weekly psychotherapy. That's what I recommended and what Winthrop agreed to and complied with.

Winthrop Cohen's clinical depression responded to a short course of antidepressant medication and psychodynamic psychotherapy focused on clarifying and interpreting his wartime trauma in the context of his biography and intimate relations. After eight weeks, he no longer stared off into space or looked agitated or seriously depressed. He returned to work. His wife and daughter thanked me for treating this "breakdown." But Winthrop Cohen never thanked me. To the contrary, at our last meeting, he implied that I was part of the societal collusion to cover up the threatening implications of war experiences such as his.

"I can put it away again. I don't feel the same pressure. I can sleep, and eat, and fornicate again. But you know as well as I do that what's bothering me can't be treated or cured. Job said: 'I will maintain my integrity. I will hold on to my righteousness.' I did neither. I soiled myself as I was soiled. I lost my humanity as those around me did the same. You don't have any answers. Nor do I. Save to live with it. To realize I did the worst is to understand how ordinary men do bad things. How ordinary Americans were so anti-Semitic at that time. How ordinary Germans did what they did during the Holocaust. How all of us are capable of murder. In the midst of war when all hell breaks loose and you are empowered to act with impunity, you can do horror and be decorated for it. And you can dine out for decades telling war stories, stories that are untrue. Because who can face up to the reality of the evil we did? Only the patriotic memories last. The killing is forgotten. The suffering remembered, because it is legitimate to speak of it. What can't be said—I mean in public—is what I did. What does that tell you about the soul?"

Winthrop Cohen asked me this question two decades ago. I wrote it down verbatim in my clinical notes. The commentary I added alongside Winthrop's words in my notes is not worth repeating because it seems banal and disturbingly off the mark. I must have felt my clinical prowess was threatened because I commented solely on the depression and its effect, and what happened after treatment. I knew, of course, there was a larger, more telling ethical issue, but I turned away from it.

Perhaps I was misled by Winthrop Cohen's final word. Soul, after all, turns the force of his critique to the inner self as if it were isolated from the world. But everything else he said points to the world. What does that tell you about the world? It is just as damning and sounds in retrospect the right conclusion. Job referred to his inner state with the Hebrew term *ka'as,* "vexed." That is the same meaning Chinese victims of the Cultural Revolution gave to their feeling state, which they named with the term *fan zao*—vexed in the sense of being shaken by an outer force that powerfully agitates our inner state. It reminds me of the inseparable tie between our selves and our local worlds, emotion and value. And it reminds me of Winthrop Cohen, because he had been shaken by the brutal force of war and what he felt was a just response to what he had done and what had been done to him.

Eight years ago I learned from a former colleague that Winthrop Cohen had died of liver failure, the long-term consequence of the hepatitis he had contracted in the Pacific war. I went back to my clinical notes, something I do not routinely do, because I was troubled by something unfinished, ethical questions I had never addressed. I tried to rethink the case in the much wider context of twentieth-century American society. What had mattered to Winthrop Cohen was to move ahead, to succeed at a high level. His mother had set him on the course of moving from the Jewish lower middle class, to which their prospects had fallen, to the Protestant elite class that then dominated American society. She did it with the name she gave to him, the stories she told him, and the high expectation she held for him. The negative example of his father's repeated failures was masked by the positive example of his grandfather's achievement.

But Winthrop Cohen also embodied a religious ideal. He bore the mark of a people that defined itself, in his words, as special in its relation to God, in its historical sense of the elevated demands of its ethical culture, and in its stubborn struggles to square religious values with real-life problems through especially strong concern with suffering, healing, and medicine. In the radically changed ethos of battle, Winthrop Cohen had succeeded brilliantly as a warrior—a success that would be matched by his secular career, which advanced from one achievement to another. But as a human being, he had failed in his own mind in the most existential way. He had killed, and not just with professional competence but with savage explosions of rage. And he had killed someone who, he said to me, even at the moment of being killed practiced the very ethical values Winthrop Cohen associated with his own religion. He called this military doctor "innocent," "a healer." Of course we don't really know if this was so. For all we, and Winthrop, know, the Japanese medic may have participated in atrocities too. If he personally hadn't done so, other Japanese had. And of all America's wars, the war Winthrop fought in seems to come closest to the justifications of a just war. Even if we find this rationalization unappealing, Winthrop Cohen was fighting for his life. In the chaotic hell of battle he had done what he had to do, I thought, trying even in my interpretive strategy to protect this vulnerable former soldier who refused all artifice and counterargument. Wasn't his implacable self-criticism a vindication of his decency? But for Winthrop it was the existential reality of his moral imagination that counted. He had done what he could never accept. He had done more than betray his ideals; he had done something so evil there was no atonement, only punishment. He, a Jew on his way to success in the Christian world, had killed a "Christlike" figure. He said that. And my thoughts now completed the charge: he had thereby enacted a vicious myth that has been immensely destructive over so many generations. His personal tragedy, I now told myself, was deepened by the embodiment of this terribly dangerous collective myth.

For Winthrop Cohen, what mattered most at the moment of his heroism and horror was killing and avoiding being killed. He proved to others and himself that he could do it. He remembered, however, and he remembered with a vengeance. Even forty years after the event, he could put himself right back into the fighting. His memory had the purpose of taking vengeance on himself. He could not forget or forgive himself. He had justice in mind. And so we have the telling, and not uncommon, paradox of a man with mental illness (depression) giving voice to powerfully disturbing insights about the danger of ordinary life and the burden of moral responsibility that a normal man could neither think nor speak.

TO LUCASTA,
ON GOING TO THE WARS

RICHARD LOVELACE

Tell me not, Sweet, I am unkind
    That from the nunnery
Of thy chaste breast, and quiet mind
    To war and arms I fly.

True, a new mistress now I chase,
    The first foe in the field;
And with a stronger faith embrace
    A sword, a horse, a shield.

Yet this inconstancy is such
    As you, too, shall adore;
I could not love you, dear, so much,
    Loved I not honor more.

ON BEING A CRIPPLE

NANCY MAIRS

To escape is nothing. Not to escape is nothing.
— Louise Bogan

The other day I was thinking of writing an essay on being a cripple. I was thinking hard in one of the stalls of the women's room in my office building, as I was shoving my shirt into my jeans and tugging up my zipper. Preoccupied, I flushed, picked up my book bag, took my cane down from the hook, and unlatched the door. So many movements unbalanced me, and as I pulled the door open I fell over backward, landing fully clothed on the toilet seat with my legs splayed in front of me: the old beetle-on-its-back routine. Saturday afternoon, the building deserted, I was free to laugh aloud as I wriggled back to my feet, my voice bouncing off the yellowish tiles from all directions. Had anyone been there with me, I'd have been still and faint and hot with chagrin. I decided that it was high time to write the essay.

First, the matter of semantics. I am a cripple. I choose this word to name me. I choose from among several possibilities, the most common of which are "handi-capped" and "disabled." I made the choice a number of years ago, without thinking, unaware of my motives for doing so. Even now, I'm not sure what those motives are, but I recognize that they are complex and not entirely flattering. People—crippled or not—wince at the word "cripple," as they do not at "handicapped" or "disabled." Perhaps I want them to wince. I want them to see me as a tough customer, one to whom the fates/gods/viruses have not been kind, but who can face the brutal truth of her existence squarely. As a cripple, I swagger.

But, to be fair to myself, a certain amount of honesty underlies my choice. "Cripple" seems to me a clean word, straightforward and precise. It has an honorable history, having made its first appearance in the Lindisfarne Gospel in the tenth century. As a lover of words, I like the accuracy with which it describes my condition: I have lost the full use of my limbs. "Disabled," by contrast, suggests any incapacity, physi-cal or mental. And I certainly don't like "handicapped," which implies that I have deliberately been put at a disadvantage, by whom I can't imagine (my God is not a Handicapper General), in order to equalize chances in the great race of life. These words seem to me to be moving away from my condition, to be widening the gap between word and reality. Most remote is the recently coined euphemism "differently abled," which partakes of the same semantic hopefulness that transformed countries from "undeveloped" to "underdeveloped," then to "less developed," and finally to "developing" nations. People have continued to starve in those countries during the shift. Some realities do not obey the dictates of language.

Mine is one of them. Whatever you call me, I remain crippled. But I don't care what you call me, so long as it isn't "differently abled," which strikes me as pure verbal garbage designed, by its ability to describe anyone, to describe no one. I subscribe to George Orwell's thesis that "the slovenliness of our language makes it easier for us to have foolish thoughts." And I refuse to participate in the degeneration of the language to the extent that I deny that I have lost anything in the course of this calamitous disease; I refuse to pretend that the only differences between you and me are the various ordinary ones that distinguish any one person from another. But call me "disabled" or "handicapped" if you like. I have long since grown accustomed to them; and if they are vague, at least they hint at the truth. Moreover, I use them myself. Society is no readier to accept crippledness than to accept death, war, sex, sweat, or wrinkles. I would never refer to another person as a cripple. It is a word I use to name only myself.

I haven't always been crippled, a fact for which I am soundly grateful. To be whole of limb is, I know from experience, infinitely more pleasant and useful than to be crippled; and if that knowledge leaves me open to bitterness at my loss, the physical soundness I once enjoyed (though I did not enjoy it half enough) is well worth the occasional stab of regret. Though never any good at sports, I was a normally active child and young adult. I climbed trees, played hopscotch, jumped rope, skated, swam, rode my bicycle, sailed. I despised team sports, spending some of the wretchedest afternoons of my life, sweaty and humiliated, behind a field-hockey stick and under a basketball hoop. I tramped alone for miles along the bridle paths that webbed the woods behind the house I grew up in. I swayed through countless dim hours in the arms of one man or another under the scattered shot of light from mirrored balls, and gyrated through countless more as Tab Hunter and Johnny Mathis gave way to the Rolling Stones, Creedence Clearwater Revival, Cream. I walked down the aisle. I pushed baby carriages, changed tires in the rain, marched for peace.

When I was twenty-eight I started to trip and drop things. What at first seemed my natural clumsiness soon became too pronounced to shrug off. I consulted a neurologist, who told me I had a brain tumor. A battery of tests, increasingly disagreeable, revealed no tumor. About a year and a half later I developed a blurred spot in one eye. I had, at last, the episodes "disseminated in space and time" requisite for a diagnosis: multiple sclerosis. I have never been sorry for the doctor's initial misdiagnosis, however.

For almost a week, until the negative results of the tests were in, I thought that I was going to die right away. Every day for the past nearly ten years, then, has been a kind of gift. I accept all gifts.

Multiple sclerosis is a chronic degenerative disease of the central nervous system, in which the myelin that sheathes the nerves is somehow eaten away and scar tissue forms in its place, interrupting the nerves' signals. During its course, which is un-predictable and uncontrollable, one may lose vision, hearing, speech, the ability to walk, control of bladder and/or bowels, strength in any or all extremities, sensitivity to touch, vibration, and/or pain, potency, coordination of movements—the list of possibilities is lengthy and, yes, horrifying. One may also lose one's sense of humor. That's the easiest to lose and the hardest to survive without.

In the past ten years, I have sustained some of these losses. Characteristic of MS are sudden attacks, called exacerbations, followed by remissions, and these I have not had. Instead, my disease has been slowly progressive. My left leg is now so weak that I walk with the aid of a brace and a cane; and for distances I use an Amigo, a variation on the electric wheelchair that looks rather like an electrified kiddie car. I no longer have much use of my left hand. Now my right side is weakening as well. I still have the blurred spot in my right eye. Overall, though, I've been lucky so far. My world has, of necessity, been circumscribed by my losses, but the terrain left me has been ample enough for me to continue many of the activities that absorb me: writing, teaching, raising children and cats and plants and snakes, reading, speaking publicly about MS and depression, even playing bridge with people patient and honorable enough to let me scatter cards every which way without sneaking a peek.

Lest I begin to sound like Pollyanna, however, let me say that I don't like having MS. I hate it. My life holds realities—harsh ones, some of them—that no right-minded human being ought to accept without grumbling. One of them is fatigue. I know of no one with MS who does not complain of bone-weariness; in a disease that presents an astonishing variety of symptoms, fatigue seems to be a common factor. I wake up in the morning feeling the way most people do at the end of a bad day, and I take it from there. As a result, I spend a lot of time *in extremis* and, impatient with limitation, I tend to ignore my fatigue until my body breaks down in some way and forces rest. Then I miss picnics, dinner parties, poetry readings, the brief visits of old friends from out of town. The offspring of a puritanical tradition of exceptional venerability, I cannot view these lapses without shame. My life often seems a series of small failures to do as I ought.

I lead, on the whole, an ordinary life, probably rather like the one I would have led had I not had MS. I am lucky that my predilections were already solitary, seden-tary, and bookish—unlike the world-famous French cellist I have read about, or the young woman I talked with one long afternoon who wanted only to be a jockey. I had just begun graduate school when I found out something was wrong with me, and I have remained, interminably, a graduate student. Perhaps I would not have if I'd thought I had the stamina to return to a full-time job as a technical editor; but I've enjoyed my studies.

In addition to studying, I teach writing courses. I also teach medical students how to give neurological examinations. I pick up freelance editing jobs here and there. I have raised a foster son and sent him into the world, where he has made me two grandbabies, and I am still escorting my daughter and son through adolescence. I go to Mass every Saturday. I am a superb, if messy, cook. I am also an enthusiastic laundress, capable of sorting a hamper full of clothes into five subtly differentiated piles, but a terrible housekeeper. I can do italic writing and, in an emergency, bathe an oil-soaked cat. I play a fiendish game of Scrabble. When I have the time and the money, I like to sit on my front steps with my husband, drinking Amaretto and smoking a cigar, as we imagine our counterparts in Leningrad and make sure that the sun gets down once more behind the sharp childish scrawl of the Tucson Mountains.

This lively plenty has its bleak complement, of course, in all the things I can no longer do. I will never run again, except in dreams, and one day I may have to write that I will never walk again. I like to go camping, but I can't follow George and the children along the trails that wander out of a campsite through the desert or into the mountains. In fact, even on the level I've learned never to check the weather or try to hold a coherent conversation: I need all my attention for my wayward feet. Of late, I have begun to catch myself wondering how people can propel themselves without canes. With only one usable hand, I have to select my clothing with care not so much for style as for ease of ingress and egress, and even so, dressing can be laborious. I can no longer do fine stitchery, pick up babies, play the piano, braid my hair. I am immobilized by acute attacks of depression, which may or may not be physiologically related to MS but are certainly its logical concomitant.

These two elements, the plenty and the privation, are never pure, nor are the delight and wretchedness that accompany them. Almost every pickle that I get into as a result of my weakness and clumsiness—and I get into plenty—is funny as well as maddening and sometimes painful. I recall one May afternoon when a friend and I were going out for a drink after finishing up at school. As we were climbing into opposite sides of my car, chatting, I tripped and fell, flat and hard, onto the asphalt parking lot, my abrupt departure interrupting him in mid-sentence. "Where'd you go?" he called as he came around the back of the car to find me hauling myself up by the door frame. "Are you all right?" Yes, I told him, I was fine, just a bit rattly, and we drove off to find a shady patio and some beer. When I got home an hour or so later, my daughter greeted me with "What have you done to yourself?" I looked down. One elbow of my white turtleneck with the green froggies, one knee of my white trousers, one white kneesock were bloodsoaked. We peeled off the clothes and inspected the damage, which was nasty enough but not alarming. That part wasn't funny: The abrasions took a long time to heal, and one got a little infected. Even so, when I think of my friend talking earnestly, suddenly, to the hot thin air while

I dropped from his view as though through a trap door, I find the image as silly as something from a Marx Brothers movie.

I may find it easier than other cripples to amuse myself because I live propped by the acceptance and the assistance and, sometimes, the amusement of those around me. Grocery clerks tear my checks out of my checkbook for me, and sales clerks find chairs to put into dressing rooms when I want to try on clothes. The people I work with make sure I teach at times when I am least likely to be fatigued, in places I can get to, with the materials I need. My students, with one anonymous exception (in an end-of-the-semester evaluation), have been unperturbed by my disability. Some even like it. One was immensely cheered by the information that I paint my own finger-nails; she decided, she told me, that if I could go to such trouble over fine details, she could keep on writing essays. I suppose I became some sort of bright-fingered muse. She wrote good essays, too.

The most important struts in the framework of my existence, of course, are my husband and children. Dismayingly few marriages survive the MS test, and why should they? Most twenty-two- and nineteen-year-olds, like George and me, can vow in clear conscience, after a childhood of chicken pox and summer colds, to keep one another in sickness and in health so long as they both shall live. Not many are equipped for catastrophe: the dismay, the depression, the extra work, the boredom that a degenerative disease can insinuate into a relationship. And our society, with its emphasis on fun and its association of fun with physical performance, offers little encouragement for a whole spouse to stay with a crippled partner. Children experience similar stresses when faced with a crippled parent, and they are more helpless, since parents and children can't usually get divorced. They hate, of course, to be different from their peers, and the child whose mother is tacking down the aisle of a school auditorium packed with proud parents like a Cape Cod dinghy in a stiff breeze jolly well stands out in a crowd. Deprived of legal divorce, the child can at least deny the mother's disability, even her existence, forgetting to tell her about recitals and PTA meetings, refusing to accompany her to stores or church or the movies, never inviting friends to the house. Many do.

But I've been limping along for ten years now, and so far George and the children are still at my left elbow, holding tight. Anne and Matthew vacuum floors and dust furniture and haul trash and rake up dog droppings and button my cuffs and bake lasagna and Toll House cookies with just enough grumbling so I know that they don't have brain fever. And far from hiding me, they're forever dragging me by racks of fancy clothes or through teeming school corridors, or welcoming gaggles of friends while I'm wandering through the house in Anne's filmy pink babydoll pajamas. George generally calls before he brings someone home, but he does just as many dumb thankless chores as the children. And they all yell at me, laugh at some of my jokes, write me funny letters when we're apart—in short, treat me as an ordinary human being for whom they have some use. I think they like me. Unless they're faking…

Faking. There's the rub. Tugging at the fringes of my consciousness always is the terror that people are kind to me only because I'm a cripple. My mother almost shattered me once, with that instinct mothers have—blind, I think in this case, but unerring nonetheless—for striking blows along the fault-lines of their children's hearts, by telling me, in an attack on my selfishness, "We all have to make allowances for you, of course, because of the way you are." From the distance of a couple of years, I have to admit that I haven't any idea just what she meant, and I'm not sure that she knew either. She was awfully angry. But at the time, as the words thudded home, I felt my worst fear, suddenly realized. I could bear being called selfish: I am. But I couldn't bear the corroboration that those around me were doing in fact what I'd always suspected them of doing, professing fondness while silently putting up with me because of the way I am. A cripple. I've been a little cracked ever since.

Along with this fear that people are secretly accepting shoddy goods comes a relentless pressure to please—to prove myself worth the burdens I impose, I guess, or to build a substantial account of goodwill against which I may write drafts in times of need. Part of the pressure arises from social expectations. In our society, anyone who deviates from the norm had better find some way to compensate. Like fat people, who are expected to be jolly, cripples must bear their lot meekly and cheerfully. A grumpy cripple isn't playing by the rules. And much of the pressure is self-generated. Early on I vowed that, if I had to have MS, by God I was going to do it well. This is a class act, ladies and gentlemen. No tears, no recriminations, no faint-heartedness.

One way and another, then, I wind up feeling like Tiny Tim, peering over the edge of the table at the Christmas goose, waving my crutch, piping down God's blessing on us all. Only sometimes I don't want to play Tiny Tim. I'd rather be Caliban, a most scurvy monster. Fortunately, at home no one much cares whether I'm a good cripple or a bad cripple as long as I make vichyssoise with fair regularity. One evening several years ago, Anne was reading at the dining-room table while I cooked dinner. As I opened a can of tomatoes, the can slipped in my left hand and juice spattered me and the counter with bloody spots. Fatigued and infuriated, I bellowed, "I'm so sick of being crippled!" Anne glanced at me over the top of her book. "There now," she said, "do you feel better?" "Yes," I said, "yes, I do." She went back to her reading. I felt better. That's about all the attention my scurviness ever gets.

Because I hate being crippled, I sometimes hate myself for being a cripple. Over the years I have come to expect—even accept—attacks of violent self-loathing. Luckily, in general our society no longer connects deformity and disease directly with evil (though a charismatic once told me that I have MS because a devil is in me) and so I'm allowed to move largely at will, even among small children. But I'm not sure that this revision of attitude has been particularly helpful. Physical imperfection, even freed of moral disapprobation, still defies and violates the ideal, especially for women, whose confinement in their bodies as objects of desire is far from over. Each age, of course, has its ideal, and I doubt that ours is any better or worse than any other. Today's ideal woman, who lives on the glossy pages of dozens of magazines, seems to be between the ages of eighteen and twenty-five; her hair has body, her teeth flash white, her breath smells minty, her underarms are dry; she has a career but is still a fabulous cook, especially of meals that take less than twenty minutes to prepare; she does not ordinarily appear to have a husband or children; she is trim and deeply tanned; she jogs, swims, plays tennis, rides a bicycle, sails, but does not bowl; she travels widely, even to out-of-the-way places like Finland and Samoa, always in the company of the ideal man, who possesses a nearly identical set of characteristics. There are a few exceptions. Though usually white and often blonde, she may be black, Hispanic, Asian, or Native American, so long as she is unusually sleek. She may be old, provided she is selling a laxative or is Lauren Bacall. If she is selling a detergent, she may be married and have a flock of strikingly messy children. But she is never a cripple.

Like many women I know, I have always had an uneasy relationship with my body. I was not a popular child, largely, I think now, because I was peculiar: intelligent, intense, moody, shy, given to unexpected actions and inexplicable notions and emotions. But as I entered adolescence, I believed myself unpopular because I was homely: my breasts too flat, my mouth too wide, my hips too narrow, my clothing never quite right in fit or style. I was not, in fact, particularly ugly, old photographs inform me, though I was well off the ideal; but I carried this sense of self-alienation with me into adulthood, where it regenerated in response to the depredations of MS. Even with my brace I walk with a limp so pronounced that, seeing myself on the videotape of a television program on the disabled, I couldn't believe that anything but an inchworm could make progress humping along like that. My shoulders droop and my pelvis thrusts forward as I try to balance myself upright throwing my frame into a bony S. As a result of contractures, one shoulder is higher than the other and I carry one arm bent in front of me, the fingers curled into a claw. My left arm and leg have wasted into pipe-stems, and I try always to keep them covered. When I think about how my body must look to others, especially to men, to whom I have been trained to display myself, I feel ludicrous, even loathsome.

At my age, however, I don't spend much time thinking about my appearance. The burning egocentricity of adolescence, which assures one that all the world is looking all the time, has passed, thank God, and I'm generally too caught up in what I'm doing to step back, as I used to, and watch myself as though upon a stage. I'm also too old to believe in the accuracy of self-image. I know that I'm not a hideous crone, that in fact, when I'm rested, well dressed, and well made up, I look fine. The self-loathing I feel is neither physically nor intellectually substantial. What I hate is not me but a disease.

I am not a disease.

And a disease is not—at lease not singlehandedly—going to determine who I am, though at first it seemed to be going to. Adjusting to a chronic incurable illness,

I have moved through a process similar to that outlined by Elizabeth Kübler-Ross in *On Death and Dying.* The major difference—and it is far more significant than most people recognize—is that I can't be sure of the outcome, as the terminally ill cancer patient can. Research studies indicate that, with proper medical care, I may achieve a "normal" life span. And in our society, with its vision of death as the ultimate evil, worse even than decrepitude, the response to such news is, "Oh well, at least you're not going to *die.*" Are there worse things than dying? I think that there may be.

I think of two women I know, both with MS, both enough older than I to have served me as models. One took to her bed several years ago and has been there ever since. Although she can sit in a high-backed wheelchair, because she is incontinent she refuses to go out at all, even though incontinence pants, which are readily available at any pharmacy, could protect her from embarrassment. Instead, she stays at home and insists that her husband, a small quiet man, a retired civil servant, stay there with her except for a quick weekly foray to the supermarket. The other woman, whose illness was diagnosed when she was eighteen, a nursing student engaged to a young doctor, finished her training, married her doctor, accompanied him to Germany when he was in the service, bore three sons and a daughter, now grown and gone. When she can, she travels with her husband; she plays bridge, embroiders, swims regularly; she works, like me, as a symptomatic-patient instructor of medical students in neurology. Guess which woman I hope to be.

At the beginning, I thought about having MS almost incessantly. And because of the unpredictable course of the disease, my thoughts were always terrified. Each night I'd get into bed wondering whether I'd get out again the next morning, whether I'd be able to see, to speak, to hold a pen between my fingers. Knowing that the day might come when I'd be physically incapable of killing myself, I thought perhaps I ought to do so right away, while I still had the strength. Gradually I came to understand that the Nancy who might one day lie inert under a bedsheet, arms and legs paralyzed, unable to feed or bathe herself, unable to reach out for a gun, a bottle of pills, was not the Nancy I was at present, and that I could not presume to make decisions for that future Nancy, who might well not want in the least to die. Now the only provision I've made for the future Nancy is that when the time comes—and it is likely to come in the form of pneumonia, friend to the weak and the old—I am not to be treated with machines and medications. If she is unable to communicate by then, I hope she will be satisfied with these terms.

Thinking all the time about having MS grew tiresome and intrusive, especially in the large and tragic mode in which I was accustomed to considering my plight. Months and even years went by without catastrophe (at least without one related to MS), and really I was awfully busy, what with George and the children and snakes and students and poems, and I hadn't the time, let alone the inclination, to devote myself to being a disease. Too, the richer my life became, the funnier it seemed, as though there were some connection between largesse and laughter, and so my tragic stance began to waver until, even with the aid of a brace and a cane, I couldn't hold it for very long at a time.

After several years I was satisfied with my adjustment. I had suffered my grief and fury and terror, I thought, but now I was at ease with my lot. Then one summer day I set out with George and the children across the desert for a vacation in California. Part way to Yuma I became aware that my right leg felt funny. "I think I've had an exacerbation," I told George. "What shall we do?" he asked. "I think we'd better get the hell to California," I said, "because I don't know whether I'll ever make it again." So we went on to San Diego and then to Orange, up the Pacific Coast Highway to Santa Cruz, across to Yosemite, down to Sequoia and Joshua Tree, and so back over the desert to home. It was a fine two-week trip, filled with friends and fair weather, and I wouldn't have missed it for the world, though I did in fact make it back to California two years later. Nor would there have been any point in missing it, since in MS, once the symptoms have appeared, the neurological damage has been done, and there's no way to predict or prevent that damage.

The incident spoiled my self-satisfaction, however. It renewed my grief and fury and terror, and I learned that one never finishes adjusting to MS. I don't know now why I thought one would. One does not, after all, finish adjusting to life, and MS is simply a fact of my life—not my favorite fact, of course—but as ordinary as my nose and my tropical fish and my yellow Mazda station wagon. It may at any time get worse, but no amount of worry or anticipation can prepare me for a new loss. My life is a lesson in losses. I learn one at a time.

And I had best be patient in the learning, since I'll have to do it like it or not. As any rock fan knows, you can't always get what you want. Particularly when you have MS. You can't, for example, get cured. In recent years researchers and the organizations that fund research have started to pay MS some attention even though it isn't fatal; perhaps they have begun to see that life is something other than a quantitative phenomenon, that one may be very much alive for a very long time in a life that isn't worth living. The researchers have made some progress toward understanding the mechanism of the disease: It may well be an autoimmune reaction triggered by a slow-acting virus. But they are nowhere near its prevention, control, or cure. And most of us want to be cured. Some, unable to accept incurability, grasp at one treatment after another, no matter how bizarre: megavitamin therapy, gluten-free diet, injections of cobra venom, hypothermal suits, lymphocytopharesis, hyperbaric chambers. Many treatments are probably harmless enough, but none are curative.

The absence of a cure often makes MS patients bitter toward their doctors. Doctors are, after all, the priests of modern society, the new shamans, whose business is to heal, and many an MS patient roves from one to another, searching for the "good" doctor who will make him well. Doctors too think of themselves as healers, and for this reason many have trouble dealing with MS patients, whose disease in its intransigence defeats their aims and mocks their skills. Too few doctors, it is true, treat their patients as whole human beings, but the reverse is also true. I have always tried to be gentle with my doctors, who often have more at stake in terms of ego than I do. I may be frustrated, maddened, depressed by the incurability of my disease, but I am not diminished by it, and they are. When I push myself up from my seat in the waiting room and stumble toward them, I incarnate the limitation of their powers. The least I can do is refuse to press on their tenderest spots.

This gentleness is part of the reason that I'm not sorry to be a cripple. I didn't have it before. Perhaps I'd have developed it anyway—how could I know such a thing?—and I wish I had more of it, but I'm glad of what I have. It has opened and enriched my life enormously, this sense that my frailty and need must be mirrored in others, that in searching for and shaping a stable core in a life wrenched by change and loss, change and loss, I must recognize the same process, under individual conditions, in the lives around me. I do not deprecate such knowledge, however I've come by it.

All the same, if a cure were found, would I take it? In a minute. I may be a cripple, but I'm only occasionally a loony and never a saint. Anyway, in my brand of theology God doesn't give bonus points for a limp. I'd take a cure; I just don't need one. A friend who also has MS startled me once by asking, "Do you ever say to yourself, 'Why me, Lord?'" "No, Michael, I don't," I told him, "because whenever I try, the only response I can think of is 'Why not?'" If I could make a cosmic deal, who would I put in my place? What in my life would I give up in exchange for sound limbs and a thrilling rush of energy? No one. Nothing. I might as well do the job myself. Now that I'm getting the hang of it.

THE PROMISE

VENETA MASSON

If you could just lose weight
your blood pressure would go down
your diabetes would clear up
you could get off all those pills you take
your joints wouldn't ache
you could climb the stairs
run after the bus
carry the groceries
pick up the baby
the swelling in your legs would go down
you could reach all the way to your aching feet
you could breathe again

You could find clothes to fit
get out of those slippers and into real shoes
who knows but what your old man would come back
you'd get more respect from your children
a decent job
your son would kick drugs
your daughter wouldn't get pregnant again
you'd live to see your last one grown

Your neighbors wouldn't talk about you
the toilet would flush
the roof wouldn't leak
there'd be food enough at the end of the month
they wouldn't cut off your check
jack up the rent
you'd hit the number
go off for two weeks in Aruba

Jesus would save the world from sin
those who mourn would be comforted
the poor would enter the Kingdom of God
your hunger would be filled.

STAR-FIX

MARILYN NELSON

For Melvin M. Nelson, Captain USAF (ret.)
(1917 – 1966)

At his cramped desk
under the astrodome,
the navigator looks
thousands of light-years
everywhere but down.
He gets a celestial fix,
measuring head-winds;
checking the log;
plotting wind-speed,
altitude, drift
in a circle of protractors,
slide-rules, and pencils.

He charts in his Howgozit
the points of no alternate
and of no return.
He keeps his eyes on the compass,
the two altimeters, the map.
He thinks, *Do we have enough fuel?*
What if my radio fails?

He's the only Negro in the crew.
The only black flyer on the whole base,
for that matter. Not that it does:
this crew is a team.
Bob and Al, Les, Smitty, Nelson.

Smitty, who said once
after a poker game,
I love you, Nelson.
I never thought I could love
a colored man.
When we get out of this man's Air Force,
if you ever come down to Tuscaloosa,
look me up and come to dinner.
You can come in the front door, too;
hell, you can stay overnight!
Of course, as soon as you leave,
I'll have to burn down my house.
Because if I don't my neighbors will.

The navigator knows where he is
because he knows where he's been
and where he's going.
At night, since he can't fly
by dead-reckoning,
he calculates his position
by shooting a star.

The octant tells him
the angle of a fixed star
over the artificial horizon.
His position in that angle
is absolute and true:
Where the hell are we, Nelson?
Alioth, in the Big Dipper.
Regulus. Antares, in Scorpio.

He plots their lines
of position on the chart,
gets his radio bearing,
corrects for lost time.

Bob, Al, Les, and Smitty
are counting on their navigator.
If he sleeps,
they all sleep.
If he fails
they fall.

The navigator keeps watch
over the night and the instruments,
going hungry for five or six hours
to give his flight-lunch
to his two little girls.

FREEMAN FIELD

MARILYN NELSON

For Edward Wilson Woodward, Captain USAF (ret.)
and the 101 of the 477th

It was a cool evening
in the middle of April.
The 477th, the only Negro
bombadier group in the Air Corps,
had just been transferred
to Freeman Field.

Some of the guys
said they were hungry
and left to find food.
The others went on
playing bridge,
mending socks,
writing letters home.

A few minutes later
the hungry guys came back,
still hungry.
We're under arrest.

The others thought they were kidding.

The next morning
the Base Commander
issued new regulations:
Negro officers were assigned
to the NCO Club;
white officers were assigned
to the Officers' Club.

The Base Commander,
who had deliberately busted
an entire Negro outfit
so he wouldn't have to be
their flight-leader in combat,
was a graduate of West Point.

He issued a statement:
If we do not allow
Negro and white officers to mix,
the accident rate
will go down two
and two-tenths
percent.

Sixty-one Negro officers
were ordered to report
one by one
to his office.
Lieutenant, have you read the regulations?
Sign here if you have read and understood.

Sixty-one Negro officers
refused to sign.
A man of your intelligence
must be able to recognize
the dangers of fraternization.

They refused to sign.
This is an order:
Sign the document.

They refused to sign.
This is a direct order!
You will sign the document!

Six cargo planes were called in;
pilots, navigators, and bombadiers
were shoved on board and flown
to Godman Field, Kentucky.

Across the river
was Fort Knox.
The sixty-one
had grown by now
to one hundred and one
American fliers trained
to fight Nazis.
They were confined
to the BOQ
under guard
of armed MP's.

By night, searchlights watched
every window. By daylight
the men leaned in the windows
to smoke, watching
the German POW's pump gas,
wash windshields
and laugh
at the motorpool
across the street.

THREE MEN IN A TENT

MARILYN NELSON

For Rufus C. Mitchell

My one blood-uncle laughs
and shakes his handsome head.
Yeah, that was Ol' Corbon.
He was your daddy's classmate,
you know: They went to school together
at Wilberforce.

Seemed like Ol' Corbon
was in trouble all the time.
We slept two guys to a tent,
you know, and seemed like nobody
wanted to bunk with Ol' Corbon.
He was such a hard-luck case;
the guys thought he was jinxed.

Finally, he came to me and Dillard
—Dillard was my tent-mate—
and asked if he could bunk with us,
because he knew your dad.
He said he'd sleep
at the foot of our tent.
Dillard said, *Shit, man,*
but I talked him over.

We were on Cape Bon, Tunisia,
you know, and we had to take turns
doing guard-duty.
The Germans parachuted soldiers in
almost every night,
and they knifed men
sleeping in their tents.

One night it was Ol' Corbon's turn,
and he fell asleep on duty.
You know,
you can be shot
for doing that in combat.
But Ol' Corbon bailed himself out;
he bought life
with his black mother-wit.

The water there
was corroding the cooling systems.
If they rusted too much,
the planes couldn't fly.
Most of the pilots
—Negro and white—
were just sitting around.
The ground-crews were going crazy,
but what could we do?
You had to use water,
and the corrosive water
was the only water we had.

Then Ol' Corbon remembered
that they'd had to build a distillery
to make distilled water
for the chemistry lab at Wilberforce.
Hey, man, he told me,
I think we can do that.
So we rag-patched one together
and got our boys
back in the air.

The Commanding Officer came over
to find out why the colored boys could fly,
and Ol' Corbon explained our distillery.

Then there were the spark-plug cleaners.
You know, it's easy in the States
to clean spark plugs:
you just use a spark-plug cleaner.
But we didn't have spark-plug cleaners;
they were back in the States.
The planes were grounded again
while we waited.
Thirty to sixty days,
they said it would take.

But Ol' Corbon said
Hey, man,
I bet we can make one.
You want to try?

Well, it turns out
to be pretty simple
to make a spark-plug cleaner.
You just take a big can,
fill it with desert sand,
make a space at the top
for a spark-plug,
and blast high-pressure air
through a hole in the side.

You know, the first time
I saw General Eisenhower
was when he flew in
to find out why
the 99th was flying.

The CO introduced Staff Sergeant Corbon.

A little while later
Cape Bon Airfield
was integrated.
We were five men to a tent:
one of us
to four
of them.

I sure missed
my old buddies.
I even missed
Ol' Corbon.

PORTER

MARILYN NELSON

For Bertram Wilson, Lieutenant Colonel USAF (ret.)
and for all of my "uncles"

Suddenly
when I hear airplanes overhead—
big, silver ones
whose muscles fill the sky—
I listen: That sounds like
someone I know.
And the sky
looks much closer.

I know my intimacy, now,
with the wheel and roar
of wind around wings.
Hello, wind.
Take care of my people.
The moon and stars
aren't so white now;
some of my people
know their first names.
Hey, Arcturus.
What's happening, Polaris?
Daddy said I should look you up.

You're even
more
dumb-founding
than he told me you were.

This is my other heritage:
I have roots in the sky.
The Tuskegee Airmen
are my second family.
This new, brave,
decorated tribe.

My family.
My homeplace, at last.
It was there
all through time.
I only had
to raise my eyes.

Tuskegee Airmen,
uncles of my childhood,
how shall I live and work
to match your goodness?
Can I do more
than murmur name upon name,
as the daughter
of a thousand proud fathers?

Jefferson.
Wilson.
Sparks.
Toliver.
Woodward.
Mitchell.
Price.
Lacy.
Straker.
Smith.
Washington.
Meriweather.
White…

> One time, this was in the Sixties,
> and I was a full-bird Colonel,
> they called me in Kentucky
> and asked me to pick up
> an aircraft somebody had crashed
> down in Louisiana.

I was suppose to fly it
to a base in New Mexico
and go back to Kentucky
on a commercial flight.

It's tricky business,
flying a plane that's been crashed.
You can never tell
what might still be wrong with it.

Okay, I flew the plane to New Mexico
and got on a flight back home.
I was in full dress-uniform,
decorations and medals
and shit
all over my chest.
The Distinguished Flying Cross
with two Bronze Oak Leaf Clusters,
The Bronze Star,
a couple of commendation medals,
a European-African-Middle East Campaign Medal
with four Bronze Service Stars…

When we landed in Chicago
I was standing in the aisle
when a lady—
a little grayhaired white lady—
asked me to lift
her suitcase down.
I said, *Of course,*
and carried it on out
into the terminal for her.
When I put it down
she handed me a dime
as a tip.

He looks down.
Then he looks at me and grins.

   I TOOK it, too!

MY OEDIPUS COMPLEX

FRANK O'CONNOR

Father was in the army all through the war—the first war, I mean—so, up to the age of five, I never saw much of him, and what I saw did not worry me. Sometimes I woke and there was a big figure in khaki peering down at me in the candlelight. Sometimes in the early morning I heard the slamming of the front door and the clatter of nailed boots down the cobbles of the lane. These were Father's entrances and exits. Like Santa Claus he came and went mysteriously.

In fact, I rather liked his visits, though it was an uncomfortable squeeze between Mother and him when I got into the big bed in the early morning. He smoked, which gave him a pleasant musty smell, and shaved, an operation of astounding interest. Each time he left a trail of souvenirs—model tanks and Gurkha knives with handles made of bullet cases, and German helmets and cap badges and button-sticks, and all sorts of military equipment—carefully stowed away in a long box on top of the wardrobe, in case they ever came in handy. There was a bit of the magpie about Father; he expected everything to come in handy. When his back was turned, Mother let me get a chair and rummage through his treasures. She didn't seem to think so highly of them as he did.

The war was the most peaceful period of my life. The window of my attic faced southeast. My mother had curtained it, but that had small effect. I always woke with the first light and, with all the responsibilities of the previous day melted, feeling myself rather like the sun, ready to illumine and rejoice. Life never seemed so simple and clear and full of possibilities as then. I put my feet out from under the clothes—I called them Mrs. Left and Mrs. Right—and invented dramatic situations for them in which they discussed the problems of the day. At least Mrs. Right did; she was very demonstrative, but I hadn't the same control of Mrs. Left, so she mostly contented herself with nodding agreement.

They discussed what Mother and I should do during the day, what Santa Claus should give a fellow for Christmas, and what steps should be taken to brighten the home. There was that little matter of the baby, for instance. Mother and I could never agree about that. Ours was the only house in the terrace without a new baby, and Mother said we couldn't afford one till Father came back from the war because they cost seventeen and six. That showed how simple she was. The Geneys up the road had a baby, and everyone knew they couldn't afford seventeen and six. It was probably a cheap baby, and Mother wanted something really good, but I felt she was too exclusive. The Geneys' baby would have done us fine.

Having settled my plans for the day, I got up, put a chair under the attic window, and lifted the frame high enough to stick out my head. The window overlooked the front gardens of the terrace behind ours, and beyond these it looked over a deep valley to the tall, red-brick houses terraced up the opposite hillside, which were all still in shadow, while those at our side of the valley were all lit up, though with long strange shadows that made them seem unfamiliar; rigid and painted.

After that I went into Mother's room and climbed into the big bed. She woke and I began to tell her of my schemes. By this time, though I never seem to have noticed it, I was petrified in my nightshirt, and I thawed as I talked until, the last frost melted, I fell asleep beside her and woke again only when I heard her below in the kitchen, making the breakfast.

After breakfast we went into town, heard Mass at St. Augustine's and said a prayer for Father, and did the shopping. If the afternoon was fine we either went for a walk in the country or a visit to Mother's great friend in the convent, Mother St. Dominic. Mother had them all praying for Father, and every night, going to bed, I asked God to send him back safe from the war to us. Little, indeed, did I know what I was praying for!

One morning, I got into the big bed, and there, sure enough, was Father in his usual Santa Claus manner, but later, instead of uniform, he put on his best blue suit, and Mother was as pleased as anything. I saw nothing to be pleased about, because, out of uniform, Father was altogether less interesting, but she only beamed, and explained that our prayers had been answered, and off we went to Mass to thank God for having brought Father safely home.

The irony of it! That very day when he came in to dinner he took off his boots and put on his slippers, donned the dirty old cap he wore about the house to save him from colds, crossed his legs, and began to talk gravely to Mother, who looked anxious. Naturally, I disliked her looking anxious, because it destroyed her good looks, so I interrupted him.

"Just a moment, Larry!" she said gently.

This was only what she said when we had boring visitors, so I attached no importance to it and went on talking.

"Do be quiet, Larry!" she said impatiently. "Don't you hear me talking to Daddy?"

This was the first time I had heard those ominous words, "talking to Daddy," and I couldn't help feeling that if this was how God answers prayers, he couldn't listen to them very attentively.

"Why are you talking to Daddy?" I asked with as great show of indifference as I could muster.

"Because Daddy and I have business to discuss. Now, don't interrupt again!"

In the afternoon, at Mother's request, Father took me for a walk. This time we went into town instead of out to the country, and I thought at first, in my usual optimistic way, that it might be an improvement. It was nothing of the sort. Father and I had quite different notions of a walk in town. He had no proper interest in trams, ships, and horses, and the only thing that seemed to divert him was talking to fellows as old as himself. When I wanted to stop he simply went on, dragging me behind him by the hand; when he wanted to stop I had no alternative but to do the same. I noticed that it seemed to be a sign that he wanted to stop for a long time whenever he leaned against a wall. The second time I saw him do it I got wild. He seemed to be settling himself forever. I pulled him by the coat and trousers, but, unlike Mother who, if you were too persistent, got into a wax and said: "Larry, if you don't behave yourself, I'll give you a good slap," Father had an extraordinary capacity for amiable inattention. I sized him up and wondered would I cry, but he seemed to be too remote to be annoyed even by that. Really, it was like going for a walk with a mountain! He either ignored the wrenching and pummeling entirely, or else glanced down with a grin of amusement from his peak. I had never met anyone so absorbed in himself as he seemed.

At teatime, "talking to Daddy" began again, complicated this time by the fact that he had an evening paper, and every few minutes he put it down and told Mother something new out of it. I felt this was foul play. Man for man, I was prepared to compete with him any time for Mother's attention, but when he had it all made up for him by other people it left me no chance. Several times I tried to change the subject without success.

"You must be quiet while Daddy is reading, Larry," Mother said impatiently.

It was clear that she either genuinely liked talking to Father better than talking to me, or else that he had some terrible hold on her which made her afraid to admit the truth.

"Mummy," I said that night when she was tucking me up, "do you think if I prayed hard God would send Daddy back to the war?"

She seemed to think about that for a moment.

"No, dear," she said with a smile. "I don't think he would."

"Why wouldn't he, Mummy?"

"Because there isn't a war any longer, dear."

"But, Mummy, couldn't God make another war, if He liked?"

"He wouldn't like to, dear. It's not God who makes wars, but bad people."

"Oh!" I said.

I was disappointed about that. I began to think that God wasn't quite what he was cracked up to be.

Next morning I woke at my usual hour, feeling like a bottle of champagne. I put out my feet and invented a long conversation in which Mrs. Right talked of the trouble she had with her own father till she put him in the Home. I didn't quite know what the Home was but it sounded the right place for Father. Then I got my chair and stuck my head out of the attic window. Dawn was just breaking, with a guilty air that made me feel I had caught it in the act. My head bursting with stories and schemes, I stumbled in next door, and in the half-darkness scrambled into the big bed. There was no room at Mother's side so I had to get between her and Father. For the time being I had forgotten about him, and for several minutes I sat bolt upright, racking my brains to know what I could do with him. He was taking up more than his fair share of the bed, and I couldn't get comfortable, so I gave him several kicks that made him grunt and stretch. He made room all right, though. Mother waked and felt for me. I settled back comfortably in the warmth of the bed with my thumb in my mouth.

"Mummy!" I hummed, loudly and contentedly.

"Sssh! dear," she whispered. "Don't wake Daddy!"

This was a new development, which threatened to be even more serious than "talking to Daddy." Life without my early-morning conferences was unthinkable.

"Why?" I asked severely.

"Because poor Daddy is tired."

This seemed to me a quite inadequate reason, and I was sickened by the sentimentality of her "poor Daddy." I never liked that sort of gush; it always struck me as insincere.

"Oh!" I said lightly. Then in my most winning tone: "Do you know where I want to go with you today, Mummy?"

"No, dear," she sighed.

"I want to go down the Glen and fish for thornybacks with my new net, and then I want to go out to the Fox and Hounds, and—"

"Don't-wake-Daddy!" she hissed angrily, clapping her hand across my mouth.

But it was too late. He was awake, or nearly so. He grunted and reached for the matches. Then he stared incredulously at his watch.

"Like a cup of tea, dear?" asked Mother in a meek, hushed voice I had never heard her use before. It sounded almost as though she were afraid.

"Tea?" he exclaimed indignantly. "Do you know what the time is?"

"And after that I want to go up the Rathcooney Road," I said loudly, afraid I'd forget something in all those interruptions.

"Go to sleep at once, Larry!" she said sharply.

I began to snivel. I couldn't concentrate, the way that pair went on, and smothering my early-morning schemes was like burying a family from the cradle.

Father said nothing, but lit his pipe and sucked it, looking out into the shadows without minding Mother or me. I knew he was mad. Every time I made a remark Mother hushed me irritably. I was mortified. I felt it wasn't fair; there was even something sinister in it. Every time I had pointed out to her the waste of making two beds when we could both sleep in one, she had told me it was healthier like that, and now here was this man, this stranger, sleeping with her without the least regard for her health!

He got up early and made tea, but though he brought Mother a cup he brought none for me.

"Mummy," I shouted, "I want a cup of tea, too."

"Yes, dear," she said patiently. "You can drink from Mummy's saucer."

That settled it. Either Father or I would have to leave the house. I didn't want to drink from Mother's saucer; I wanted to be treated as an equal in my own home, so, just to spite her, I drank it all and left none for her. She took that quietly, too.

But that night when she was putting me to bed she said gently:

"Larry, I want you to promise me something."

"What is it?" I asked.

"Not to come in and disturb poor Daddy in the morning. Promise?"

"Poor Daddy" again! I was becoming suspicious of everything involving that quite impossible man.

"Why?" I asked.

"Because poor Daddy is worried and tired and he doesn't sleep well."

"Why doesn't he, Mummy?"

"Well, you know, don't you, that while he was at the war Mummy got the pennies from the Post Office!"

"From Miss MacCarthy?"

"That's right. But now, you see, Miss MacCarthy hasn't any more pennies, so Daddy must go out and find us some. You know what would happen if he couldn't?"

"No," I said, "tell us."

"Well, I think we might have to go out and beg for them like the poor old woman on Fridays. We wouldn't like that, would we?"

"No," I agreed. "We wouldn't."

"So you'll promise not to come in and wake him?"

"Promise."

Mind you, I meant that. I knew pennies were a serious matter, and I was all against having to go out and beg like the old woman on Fridays. Mother laid out all my toys in a complete ring around the bed so that, whatever way I got out, I was bound to fall over one of them.

When I woke I remembered my promise all right. I got up and sat on the floor and played—for hours, it seemed to me. Then I got my chair and looked out the attic window for more hours. I wished it was time for Father to wake; I wished someone would make me a cup of tea. I didn't feel in the least like the sun; instead, I was bored and so very, very cold! I simply longed for the warmth and depth of the big featherbed.

At last I could stand it no longer. I went into the next room. As there was still no room at Mother's side I climbed over her and she woke with a start.

"Larry," she whispered, gripping my arm very tightly, "what did you promise?"

"But I did, Mummy," I wailed, caught in the very act. "I was quiet for ever so long."

"Oh, dear, and you're perished!" she said sadly, feeling me all over. "Now if I let you stay will you promise not to talk?"

"But I want to talk, Mummy," I wailed.

"That has nothing to do with it," she said with a firmness that was new to me. "Daddy wants to sleep. Now, do you understand that?"

I understood it only too well. I wanted to talk, he wanted to sleep—whose house was it, anyway?

"Mummy," I said with equal firmness, "I think it would be healthier for Daddy to sleep in his own bed."

That seemed to stagger her, because she said nothing for a while.

"Now, once and for all," she went on, "you're to be perfectly quiet or go back to your own bed. Which is it to be?"

The injustice of it got me down. I had convicted her out of her own mouth of inconsistency and unreasonableness, and she hadn't even attempted to reply. Full of spite, I gave Father a kick, which she didn't notice but which made him grunt and open his eyes in alarm.

"What time is it?" he asked in a panic-stricken voice, not looking at Mother but at the door, as if he saw someone there.

"It's early yet," she replied soothingly. "It's only the child. Go to sleep again…. Now, Larry," she added, getting out of bed, "you've wakened Daddy and you must go back."

This time, for all her quiet air, I knew she meant it, and knew that my principal rights and privileges were as good as lost unless I asserted them at once. As she lifted me, I gave a screech, enough to wake the dead, not to mind Father. He groaned.

"That damn child! Doesn't he ever sleep?"

"It's only a habit, dear," she said quietly, though I could see she was vexed.

"Well, it's time he got out of it," shouted Father, beginning to heave in the bed. He suddenly gathered all the bedclothes about him, turned to the wall, and then looked back over his shoulder with nothing showing only two small, spiteful, dark eyes. The man looked very wicked.

To open the bedroom door, Mother had to let me down, and I broke free and dashed for the farthest corner, screeching. Father sat bolt upright in bed.

"Shut up, you little puppy!" he said in a choking voice.

I was so astonished that I stopped screeching. Never, never had anyone spoken to me in that tone before. I looked at him incredulously and saw his face convulsed with rage. It was only then that I fully realized how God had codded me, listening to my prayers for the safe return of this monster.

"Shut up, you!" I bawled, beside myself.

"What's that you said?" shouted Father, making a wild leap out of the bed.

"Mick, Mick!" cried Mother. "Don't you see the child isn't used to you?"

"I see he's better fed than taught," snarled Father, waving his arms wildly. "He wants his bottom smacked."

All his previous shouting was as nothing to these obscene words referring to my person. They really made my blood boil.

"Smack your own!" I screamed hysterically. "Smack your own! Shut up! Shut up!"

At this he lost his patience and let fly at me. He did it with the lack of conviction you'd expect of a man under Mother's horrified eyes, and it ended up as a mere tap, but the sheer indignity of being struck at all by a stranger, a total stranger who had cajoled his way back from the war into our big bed as a result of my innocent intercession, made me completely dotty. I shrieked and shrieked, and danced in my bare feet, and Father, looking awkward and hairy in nothing but a short gray army shirt, glared down at me like a mountain out for murder. I think it must have been then that I realized he was jealous too. And there stood Mother in her nightdress, looking as if her heart was broken between us. I hoped she felt as she looked. It seemed to me that she deserved it all.

From that morning out my life was hell. Father and I were enemies, open and avowed. We conducted a series of skirmishes against one another, he trying to steal my time with Mother and I his. When she was sitting on my bed, telling me a story, he took to looking for some pair of old boots which he alleged he had left behind him at the beginning of the war. While he talked to Mother I played loudly with my toys to show my total lack of concern. He created a terrible scene one evening when he came in from work and found me at his box, playing with his regimental badges, Gurkha knives and button-sticks. Mother got up and took the box from me.

"You mustn't play with Daddy's toys unless he lets you, Larry," she said severely. "Daddy doesn't play with yours."

For some reason Father looked at her as if she had struck him and then turned away with a scowl.

"Those are not toys," he growled, taking down the box again to see had I lifted anything. "Some of those curios are very rare and valuable."

But as time went on I saw more and more how he managed to alienate Mother and me. What made it worse was that I couldn't grasp his method or see what attraction he had for Mother. In every possible way he was less winning than I. He had a common accent and made noises at his tea. I thought for a while that it might be the newspapers she was interested in, so I made up bits of news of my own to read to her. Then I thought it might be the smoking, which I personally thought attractive, and took his pipes and went round the house dribbling into them till he caught me. I even made noises at my tea, but Mother only told me I was disgusting. It all seemed to hinge round that unhealthy habit of sleeping together, so I made a point of dropping into their bedroom and nosing around, talking to myself, so that they wouldn't know I was watching them, but they were never up to anything that I could see. In the end it beat me. It seemed to depend on being grown-up and giving people rings, and I realized I'd have to wait.

But at the same time I wanted him to see that I was only waiting, not giving up the fight. One evening when he was being particularly obnoxious, chattering away well above my head, I let him have it.

"Mummy," I said, "do you know what I'm going to do when I grow up?"

"No, dear," she replied. "What?"

"I'm going to marry you," I said quietly.

Father gave a great guffaw out of him, but he didn't take me in. I knew it must be only pretense. And Mother, in spite of everything, was pleased. I felt she was probably relieved to know that one day Father's hold on her would be broken.

"Won't that be nice!" she said with a smile.

"It'll be very nice," I said confidently. "Because we're going to have lots and lots of babies."

"That's right, dear," she said placidly. "I think we'll have one soon, and then you'll have plenty of company."

I was no end pleased about that because it showed that in spite of the way she gave in to Father she still considered my wishes. Besides, it would put the Geneys in their place.

It didn't turn out like that, though. To begin with, she was very preoccupied— I supposed about where she would get the seventeen and six—and though Father took to staying out late in the evenings it did me no particular good. She stopped taking me for walks, became as touchy as blazes, and smacked me for nothing at all. Sometimes I wished I'd never mentioned the confounded baby—I seemed to have a genius for bringing calamity on myself.

And calamity it was! Sonny arrived in the most appalling hullabaloo—even that much he couldn't do without a fuss—and from the first moment I disliked him. He was a difficult child—so far as I was concerned he was always difficult—and demanded far too much attention. Mother was simply silly about him, and couldn't see when he was only showing off. As company he was worse than useless. He slept all day, and I had to go round the house on tiptoe to avoid waking him. It wasn't any longer a question of not waking Father. The slogan now was "Don't-wake-Sonny!" I couldn't understand why the child wouldn't sleep at the proper time, so whenever Mother's back was turned I woke him. Sometimes to keep him awake I pinched him as well. Mother caught me at it one day and gave me a most unmerciful flaking.

One evening, when Father was coming in from work, I was playing trains in the front garden. I let on not to notice him; instead, I pretended to be talking to myself, and said in a loud voice: "If another bloody baby comes into this house, I'm going out."

Father stopped dead and looked at me over his shoulder.

"What's that you said?" he asked sternly.

"I was only talking to myself," I replied, trying to conceal my panic. "It's private."

He turned and went in without a word. Mind you, I intended it as a solemn warning, but its effect was quite different. Father started being quite nice to me. I could understand that, of course. Mother was quite sickening about Sonny. Even at mealtimes she'd get up and gawk at him in the cradle with an idiotic smile, and tell Father to do the same. He was always polite about it, but he looked so puzzled you could see he didn't know what she was talking about. He complained of the way Sonny cried at night, but she only got cross and said that Sonny never cried except when there was something up with him—which was a flaming lie, because Sonny never had anything up with him, and only cried for attention. It was really painful to see how simple-minded she was. Father wasn't attractive, but he had a fine intelligence. He saw through Sonny, and now he knew that I saw through him as well.

One night I woke with a start. There was someone beside me in bed. For one wild moment I felt sure it must be Mother, having come to her senses and left Father for good, but then I heard Sonny in convulsions in the next room, and Mother saying: "There! There! There!" and I knew it wasn't she. It was Father. He was lying beside me, wide awake, breathing hard and apparently as mad as hell.

After a while it came to me what he was mad about. It was his turn now. After turning me out of the big bed, he had been turned out himself. Mother had no consideration now for anyone but that poisonous pup, Sonny. I couldn't help feeling sorry for Father. I had been through it all myself, and even at that age I was magnanimous. I began to stroke him down and say: "There! There!" He wasn't exactly responsive.

"Aren't you asleep either?" he snarled.

"Ah, come on and put your arm around us, can't you?" I said, and he did, in a sort of way. Gingerly, I suppose, is how you'd describe it. He was very bony but better than nothing.

At Christmas he went out of his way to buy me a really nice model railway.

WAR SONG

DOROTHY PARKER

Soldier, in a curious land
    All across a swaying sea,
Take her smile and lift her hand—
    Have no guilt of me.
Soldier, when were soldiers true?
    If she's kind and sweet and gay,
Use the wish I send to you—
    Lie not lone til day!
Only, for the nights that were,
    Soldier, and the dawns that came,
When in sleep you turn to her
    Call her by my name.

SERVICE

PLATON

In the summer of 2008, the photographer
Platon took pictures of hundreds of men
and women who volunteered to serve in the
military and were sent to Iraq or Afghanistan.
He followed them on their journey through
training and deployment, after demobiliza-
tion and in hospitals, to compile a portrait
of the dedication of the armed services today.
Sergeant Tim Johannsen, who lost both legs
when he drove over an I.E.D. on his second
tour of duty in Iraq, made a point of buying
an Army T-shirt to wear in his photograph. Of
his sacrifice, he said, "It's just part of the job.
You know what you signed up for." Sergeant
Matthis Chiroux, a military reporter who has
become a vocal opponent of the Iraq war, says
that he and others like him "take our activism
as a continuation of our oath of service." Like
many who enlist, Johannsen and Chiroux come
from military families. Sergeant John McKay,
a marine whose uncle and grandfather were
marines, and whose three-year-old son posed
in uniform at the wedding of a cousin, also
a marine, said, "He's just waiting till he's
eighteen." He went on, "I'm scared for him,
but if he wants to do it I'll support him."

SEAMAN JEREMIAH LINEBERRY, JUST AFTER LOWERING THE FLAG ABOARD
THE U.S.S. SAN ANTONIO, AS HE PREPARES FOR HIS FIRST DEPLOYMENT.

CADETS MARCHING IN THE GRADUATION PARADE AT THE UNITED STATES
NINE HUNDRED CADETS GRADUATED, RECEIVING A BACHELOR-OF-SCIENCE DEGREE

MILITARY ACADEMY AT WEST POINT, MAY 30, 2008. THAT YEAR, MORE THAN
AND A COMMISSION IN THE ARMY THAT OBLIGES THEM TO SERVE FOR FIVE YEARS.

MEDINA WASL IS A MOCK IRAQI VILLAGE AT THE NATIONAL TRAINING CENTER
FROM THE FIRST STRYKER BRIGADE COMBAT TEAM OF THE 25TH INFANTRY

AT FORT IRWIN, IN THE MOJAVE DESERT, IN CALIFORNIA. THESE SOLDIERS,
DIVISION, ARE PERFORMING AN EXERCISE KNOWN AS MEDICAL TRAUMA LANE.

SEAMAN KEVIN DEAN STANDS ON THE DECK OF THE U.S.S. SAN ANTONIO,
ONE OF A NUMBER OF NEW AMPHIBIOUS TRANSPORT DOCKS, SPENT

WHICH SET SAIL ON ITS MAIDEN DEPLOYMENT ON AUGUST 28, 2008. THE SHIP,
ABOUT SIX MONTHS IN THE MEDITERRANEAN SEA AND THE PERSIAN GULF.

SERGEANT TIM JOHANNSEN AND HIS WIFE, JACQUELYNE KAY,
IN A REHABILITATION UNIT AT WALTER REED ARMY MEDICAL CENTER.

SERGEANT MATTHIS CHIROUX, HONORABLY DISCHARGED IN 2007
AFTER FIVE YEARS OF SERVICE, REFUSED TO BE REDEPLOYED TO IRAQ.

JUAN CASIANO AT THE GRAVE OF HIS FIANCÉE, CAPTAIN MARIA INES ORTIZ,
IN SECTION 60 OF ARLINGTON NATIONAL CEMETERY, WHERE THOSE KILLED
IN IRAQ AND AFGHANISTAN ARE BURIED.

ELSHEBA KHAN AT THE GRAVE OF HER SON,
SPECIALIST KAREEM RASHAD SULTAN KHAN.

AIRMAN FIRST CLASS CHRISTOPHER WILSON GREETS HIS FIANCÉE, BETH PISARSKY,
305TH SECURITY FORCES SQUADRON OF THE 305TH AIR MOBILITY

AFTER RETURNING FROM A SIX-MONTH DEPLOYMENT IN IRAQ. WILSON IS IN THE
WING, WHICH IS BASED AT MCGUIRE AIR FORCE BASE, IN NEW JERSEY.

JAKOB MCKAY, THREE, IS THE SON OF SERGEANT JOHN MCKAY,
WHO IS NOW HOME AFTER FOUR TOURS OF DUTY IN IRAQ.

JESSICA GRAY, WHOSE HUSBAND, STAFF SERGEANT YANCE GRAY,
WAS KILLED IN BAGHDAD WHILE SERVING WITH THE 82ND AIRBORNE.

BEV BROWN

SYBIL SMITH

Bev Brown is immense, approaching freight-scale proportions. It was I who, meanly, labeled her Jabba the Hut, but the other nurses laughed, and the name stuck. It is not used, of course, within her hearing.

Ridicule aside, I like Bev Brown. I am often assigned to her when she comes in.

She needs a Psych admission two or three times a year. Last week, as I took off my coat, I saw her name on the census board, which hangs above the med cart at the nurses' station. Voice discreetly pitched, I murmured to Elaine, another nurse, "Bev's back?"

"Oh ayuh," said Elaine. "In all her muumuued glory."

Whenever Bev comes in she spends the first part of her admission supine in her room, draped in the tackiest of muumuus. Cerise, ecru, chartreuse, cobalt, magenta; these are the hues her massive frame is draped in. And the material? Orlon, rayon, dacron: some slithery, shiny five-and-dime fabric. She lies in her darkened room reeking of urine (she has a stress incontinence problem), weeping, her right foot tapping like a human metronome. She has Parkinson's disease. Sometimes it's her right hand that moves (or foot and hand together) rasping rhythmically against the sheet, so that our pauses in conversation aren't quite silent.

I got the scoop in report, of course. She didn't like her job as a live-in nurse for a rich old woman. One of her sons was seriously ill. The Department of Motor Vehicles was threatening to take away her license. She couldn't take it anymore. Since she'd been admitted yesterday, she'd refused pills, food, and water. She wouldn't leave her room except to pee. It would have been easier—and was, the first part of my shift—to leave her alone, except for peeking in every hour or so.

But then came eight o'clock. Bev wouldn't take her meds.

"I don't need them," she muttered. Her back was to me, and her voice was muffled by the pillows. I knew then that I'd have to talk to her. I had the option of writing *patient refused* on the med sheet, but after all, this *was* my job. Some effort was required, and besides, I knew Bev. She could be coaxed.

I stared into the pill cup in my hand. "Clonopin," I said. "Sinemet, Colace, Imipramine, Ibuprofen. Come on, Bev, you take them all the time."

"I don't need them," she said, shifting in bed and releasing a balloon of scent. "What good are they?"

"What good are they? You know, Bev. You're an LPN."

Bev was silent, which, I suppose, I deserved, having deliberately misunderstood her. I put the pills on the bedside table and flopped into her chair. "Bev," I said, "it strikes me that you're not a happy camper."

"Brilliant," she replied.

I crossed my knees and worked the leather flat on my right foot free. Then I dangled it from my toes and admired my foot in the dim light that came through Bev's partially open door. "When you left last July, you were happy," I said. "What's been happening? I'm interested."

"My son is dying, for starters. And all Betsy ever does is ask for money. My Parkinson's is getting worse."

"How about that old lady you work for? How is that job going?"

"Crazy. You never know what she's gonna do next."

"What do you mean?"

And Bev was off and rolling. It had only taken a sum total of fifty words, spoken with a modicum of interest, to snag her. Like some massive, ornamental carp, she nosed up out of the dark bottom, toward the light. She likes to talk, is the thing. And she has a rough talent for description. She described the old lady so well I could almost hear her walker creaking through the dark halls of her fading, empty mansion, her almost defunct life. Bev does voices.

"Bev," she called in a witchy falsetto, "I have to go to the toilet." There was a pause, then, "Come quick, I have to do a big job!" Then, "Bev, what's that trash you're eating? I don't allow junk like that in my house." Then, "Bev, where are you going?" Bev's voice returned to normal and she did her own reply. "To Mars, if I'm lucky."

I laughed. "Your sense of humor is intact," I said. Bev likes to be told that. It's a point of pride with her. But even I could see that it was going to take more than a sense of humor to get her out of this one. She could watch reels of Charlie Chaplin and still be in the same boat, Norman Cousins notwithstanding.

As if reading my mind, Bev's shoulders started to shake. "Dr. Bentson's mad at me," she choked. "He asked me what I thought I was doing here this time."

"What did you say?"

"I told him I wanted to die in peace."

"But they won't let you die here," I pointed out. "People don't come to the hospital to die, unless they have terminal cancer or something."

"They can't make me eat," Bev said.

"If you keep refusing, they'll put an IV in your arm and a feeding tube down your nose."

"Hah," Bev snorted, to let me know what she thought of their puny tubes. Then she said, "If he sends me home I'll kill myself. I have enough medication to take out Burlington."

She said this with such relish that we both paused for awhile, savoring it. I could have pointed out that she was contradicting herself, but I didn't. I didn't want to hurt her dignity. Because she does have dignity. She sees herself as a tough customer, a hard-working, no-nonsense, kind-hearted woman.

She writes poems. She's shown them to me before. They are rife with misspelling but display a certain flair for metaphor. I remember, in particular, a poem to her father. Not the words, but what the words revealed. Her father started fucking her when she was fourteen. "You're a lot better at this than your mother," he told her.

She got pregnant. When she told whose it was, her mother beat her up and told the authorities she was a lying slut. She was sent to an unwed mother's home and gave the child up for adoption. After the home it was reform school, and then marriage to an abusive man. He was a construction worker and dragged his family from place to place. Bev had three more children and adopted three. Somewhere in there she got her LPN. I think that happened after her husband died—of drink. Does she miss her husband? *Hah!* That derisive *Hah* again. Fat chance. He could be hanging by the neck from that tree branch out there and she'd pull up a chair to enjoy the view.

I remember something else she told me about a tree. It was a very tall pine, down across the road, in the pasture. She would go there after her mother beat her. Her mother beat her more than she beat Bev's brother. The brother caved in, surrendered. But Bev fought back, would not submit. Her mother hit her so hard one time she broke her arm. Bev told the doctor she fell out of her tree.

She would leave the house and go down to that tree. She would climb into its topmost branches. She felt safe there. No one could touch her. She imagined she was closer to God. She saw that the world was bigger than her mother. When I start to care about Bev, I flash on that tree. I imagine her as she looks now, in a muumuu, at the very tippy top of a jack pine, gently swaying in the wind. Then I get afraid that it may break.

Somehow I had to convince her that life, in this case, was better than death, though I myself only half believed it. What was left for her after all? Her health problems were worsening. Her children had either done well and gone away, or done poorly and stayed nearby. She would end up in a nursing home herself, where the over-worked aides would hate her for her weight, her shakiness.

"You're in a tough stretch, Bev," I began. "But no matter how bad life seems, you must have hope that things will get better."

Bev was quiet, listening. Invisible antennae waved around her head.

"You're a survivor, Bev. You know that. And it's because you like to do stuff. Like write poems and buy things for your grandchildren. Remember the last time you were here? You got so excited when you found a pair of shoes you could wear.

Jogging shoes."

She was crying again. I could see her shoulders shaking. More words were needed. Alms for the poor. I had to go deeper.

And it *was* work. Because the sick aren't easy to love, nor the ugly. It's a discipline, like any other. Mother Teresa is an artist; her art, the acts of love she doles out ceaselessly.

I spoke to Bev of love and hope. I spoke to her of joy and goodness. I was a fountain of platitudes, which I hovered on the verge of believing. But occasionally an image came to me, of Bev at her medicine chest at home, gulping down pills with mouthfuls of chlorinated water. Or of Bev in the shower, dangling by her neck from the call bell. I began to entertain the logistics of the act, so to speak. There was an attraction there that I was afraid to let my heart explore. So I pushed the image away and talked on. And though one voice inside me said: *your words are crumbs, crusts, parings,* another voice said: *people can live on them. And do.*

Of course, Bev didn't spring from the bed, a new woman. She didn't flick on her light and do a jig. But she did turn toward me. It was a maneuver with many stages: a huffing, creaking rearrangement of limbs. Her mousy short hair sprouted at various angles from her head. She reached for her eyeglasses on the bedside table.

"Will you take your pills now?" I asked.

"Hand 'em over," she said. She downed the lot and chased it with water. "Thank you, Bev," I said.

She didn't reply.

"I'll be in to check on you later and talk some more. I have to give my other eight o'clocks."

Bev nodded. We had a deal now.

I left the room. I felt the way a diver must feel when he comes up too fast. Shivery. Disoriented. I went to the nurses' station. Elaine was there. She smiled at me.

"I'm an angel of mercy," I said.

"Florence Nightingale eat your heart out," she replied.

"I got Jabba to take her pills."

"Give the girl a merit raise."

"We're mean."

"But it's fun."

"You know, I was thinking something." I paused for a moment, to get it right. "When we make fun of the patients, it's like we're ducks on the shore, preening our feathers. We'd sink if we didn't."

Elaine laughed. "Not bad," she said, "as rationalizations go. Quite good actually." She closed the Land's End catalog she'd been flipping through and rose. "I'd love to stay and preen with you," she added, "but I've got to go float around in the milieu."

* * * * *

And the fact is, Bev did make it, again. I was off for a few days, and when I came back she was on a pass, shopping. When she returned she was bright-eyed and bushy-tailed. She showed me what she'd bought: mints for herself, sweatsuits for her grand-children, and a journal with a spray of fall leaves encased in polyurethane on the front. I sat in her room with her and she bustled about, breathing heavily, handing me a mint. I suddenly thought of a poem I knew by Wallace Stevens. It's called "The Final Soliloquy of the Interior Paramour." I could only remember a few lines, but they stayed with me all evening.

> *It is in that thought that we collect ourselves,*
> *Out of all the indifferences, into one thing:*
>
> *Within a single thing, a single shawl*
> *Wrapped tightly round us, since we are poor…*

I thought Bev would have understood those lines.

AN INFECTED HEART

JOHN STONE

I saw him first in April on cardiology consultation rounds. I was working with two emergency medicine residents and two cardiology fellows that month, swooping all over the hospital to see patients with suspected or clear-cut heart disease. The call over the beeper was from the burn unit.

We entered the sanctum of the unit through the swinging doors. Signs on the wall confronted us: Did you wash your hands? We did. And donned the gowns, masks, and puffy surgeons' caps that were required for the unit. We began to review the chart.

The man was young—maybe twenty-five years old—and had been burned—widely, severely. The surgeons had struggled for weeks to try to cover the burned areas with skin grafts before his wounds could become irreversibly infected. He'd been in the hospital since January—almost four months now. I thought of how much it hurts to burn a finger on a hot stove, then tried to mentally magnify it.

We listened as one of the fellows took the history: How had he been burned? The patient told us he'd been walking late one night in January when he spotted the distinctive orange glow and thick smoke of a major fire in a building he passed. He knocked loudly on the door and yelled for help. A young boy appeared at an upstairs window. The patient told us he broke in the door, roused the family out, then went back in for the boy. He'd saved the boy, but had been badly burned in the process.

The man—his name was Robert—was sitting upright in a highbacked wheelchair. His limbs, abdomen, and back were swathed in bandages; he sat propped up on foam so as to put as little pressure as possible on the tender skin underneath. From a distance, his face reminded me of one painted by Rouault: dark, broad brush stokes outlining it, another dark stroke lending prominence to the nose, and lighter tones for the rest of the face. Up close, the landscape of his face was made up of glistening caramel-colored islands of partially melted tissue; they were separated by—and seemed to be eroded by—the angry channeling red pigment of his blood that looked ready to well up at any moment from beneath the burned skin. The effect was that of a variably cooling recent lava flow. But that was not the most striking aspect of his countenance: his eyes had the look of pure terror, pupils dilated, lids widely separated—the eyes that everyone in medicine sees sooner or later. They lent to his face the unmistakable appearance of someone who's seen death and been changed by it.

We examined Robert's heart. It was racing: 160 beats a minute. There was a soft heart murmur: PfffFF . . TT, PfffFF . . TT, PfffFF . . TT. Not loud, but not normal either, we decided among ourselves.

Robert had done surprisingly well for several weeks as his own good skin was grafted over the burned areas. But then infection had set in. Antibiotics were started—first one, then two, then another set, as the bacteria became resistant to the drugs. The spiking daily fevers began—and drenching sweats. Cardiology was called to see him after bacteria were cultured from his blood. Does he have endocarditis? asked the consultation note.

We decided to do an echocardiogram. The machine was trundled up from the sixth floor of the hospital and set up in the room. An echocardiogram harks back to the sonar units used by submarines—the ones we all saw at the movies on Saturday afternoons while we were growing up, blithely unaware of any hearts but our own. The echo machine uses ultrasound waves, as does sonar, bouncing the waves off the interior anatomy of the body. Using the echo, one can visualize the heart's perpetual energy and, within it, in the swirling sea of blood, the graceful heart valves keeping the blood flowing straight and full speed ahead.

Robert's valves all looked normal, thin but with great tensile strength, smoothly opening and closing, all except the mitral valve. Instead of smoothly dancing in place, the mitral valve's motions were weighed down by a mass of heavy echoes that could mean only one thing: the blood and bacteria-laden abnormal appendages of endocarditis. His heart was infected all right, seeded from his infected burns and then itself constantly reseeding all parts of the body in its natural centrifugal energy. We were trapped and so was Robert. We might have had a better chance to cure the endocarditis had we not had the infected burns to contend with. As it was, the situation was a desperate one. We wrote out our orders and tried to explain the dilemma to Robert, being as optimistic as possible.

We saw Robert daily over the next two weeks. At first, by switching to yet another, more toxic, set of antibiotics, we seemed to be making some progress. His temperature came down—for four days it was almost normal. All the while, the surgeons worked to cover his burns with grafts. They didn't take. Robert was given several transfusions of blood. But his kidneys were beginning to fail. We adjusted medications, meeting incessantly to decide how to approach each new crisis. I could tell we were losing ground. Robert looked weaker and more resigned on each of our successive visits. The raging fever returned. He was going out in a blaze, an inferno of infection.

Several days ago, as the group of us approached the door of Robert's room, we saw that he had a visitor. The visitor's back was toward us, but his gown was open. His suit was black and, above the tie-strings of the gown around his neck, we could see the white collar of the priesthood. We backed quietly out of the room and waited. In a few minutes the priest came out, closing his Bible as he approached us, a silver cross dangling from a broad white ribbon folded over his forearm. We nodded to his nod. We examined Robert. He looked exhausted. There was a rosary in his hand. He barely noticed that we were in the room.

That afternoon the cardiology team got an emergency call to the unit. As we arrived, donning our apparel quickly, we found the entire surgical team gathered around Robert's bed, always a bad sign. Robert had had a seizure, then his heart had skipped, shuddered, and stopped. Despite our efforts, there was no way to save him. For my part, I wasn't at all sure that Robert *wanted* to be saved any longer. I thought about our sessions in ethics class on "quality of life." Robert had had little of that in the last few months.

As we left the room, a deputy sheriff was outside. He asked about Robert. We told him what had happened, that we'd lost the battle. It was only then that we learned the truth about Robert. Robert, said the deputy, was an arsonist. He had set blazes in two parts of a building back in January. But he'd gotten trapped between the two fires, was badly burned, and had barely escaped with his life by jumping from a sec- ond-story window. Robert's tale about his heroism, the young boy he'd saved, was a total lie, something he'd wanted us to believe and, in the haze of morphine, may have begun to believe himself. Ordinarily, he would have been placed under an around- the-clock guard, said the deputy; but, as he told us, "In his condition, he wasn't goin' no place."

We shrugged out of our gowns, shaking our heads in disbelief. We'd been had, all right. Robert must have figured that things would go better for him medically if his doctors thought he was a hero and not an arsonist. I like to think that knowing the truth about Robert wouldn't have affected our efforts to save him. But who can be sure of that? Robert couldn't.

THE LOTOS-EATERS

ALFRED LORD TENNYSON

"Courage!" he said, and pointed toward the land,
"This mounting wave will roll us shoreward soon."
In the afternoon they came unto a land
In which it seemed always afternoon.
All round the coast the languid air did swoon,
Breathing like one that hath a weary dream.
Full-faced above the valley stood the moon;
And like a downward smoke, the slender stream
Along the cliff to fall and pause and fall did seem.

A land of streams! some, like a downward smoke,
Slow-dropping veils of thinnest lawn, did go;
And some through wavering lights and shadows broke,
Rolling a slumbrous sheet of foam below.
They saw the gleaming river seaward flow
From the inner land: far off, three mountain-tops,
Three silent pinnacles of aged snow,
Stood sunset-flushed: and, dewed with showery drops,
Up-clomb the shadowy pine above the woven copse.

The charmed sunset lingered low adown
In the red West: through mountain clefts the dale
Was seen far inland, and the yellow down
Bordered with palm, and many a winding vale
And meadow, set with slender galingale;
A land where all things always seemed the same!
And round about the keel with faces pale,
Dark faces pale against that rosy flame,
The mild-eyed melancholy Lotos-eaters came.

Branches they bore of that enchanted stem,
Laden with flower and fruit, whereof they gave
To each, but whoso did receive of them,
And taste, to him the gushing of the wave
Far far away did seem to mourn and rave
On alien shores; and if his fellow spake,
His voice was thin, as voices from the grave;
And deep-asleep he seemed, yet all awake,
And music in his ears his beating heart did make.

They sat them down upon the yellow sand,
Between the sun and moon upon the shore;
And sweet it was to dream of Fatherland,
Of child, and wife, and slave; but evermore
Most weary seemed the sea, weary the oar,
Weary the wandering fields of barren foam.
Then some one said, "We will return no more";
And all at once they sang, "Our island home
Is far beyond the wave; we will no longer roam."

CHORIC SONG

I

There is sweet music here that softer falls
Than petals from blown roses on the grass,
Or night-dews on still waters between walls
Of shadowy granite, in a gleaming pass;
Music that gentlier on the spirit lies,
Than tired eyelids upon tired eyes;
Music that brings sweet sleep down from the blissful skies.
Here are cool mosses deep,
And through the moss the ivies creep,
And in the stream the long-leaved flowers weep,
And from the craggy ledge the poppy hangs in sleep.

II

Why are we weighed upon with heaviness,
And utterly consumed with sharp distress,
While all things else have rest from weariness?
All things have rest: why should we toil alone,
We only toil, who are the first of things,
And make perpetual moan,

Still from one sorrow to another thrown:
Nor ever fold our wings,
And cease from wanderings,
Nor steep our brows in slumber's holy balm;
Nor harken what the inner spirit sings,
"There is no joy but calm!"—
Why should we only toil, the roof and crown of things?

III

Lo! in the middle of the wood,
The folded leaf is wooed from out the bud
With winds upon the branch, and there
Grows green and broad, and takes no care,
Sun-steeped at noon, and in the moon
Nightly dew-fed; and turning yellow
Falls, and floats adown the air.
Lo! sweetened with the summer light,
The full-juiced apple, waxing over-mellow,
Drops in a silent autumn night.
All its allotted length of days,
The flower ripens in its place,
Ripens and fades, and falls, and hath no toil,
Fast-rooted in the fruitful soil.

IV

Hateful is the dark-blue sky,
Vaulted o'er the dark-blue sea.
Death is the end of life; ah, why
Should life all labor be?
Let us alone. Time driveth onward fast,
And in a little while our lips are dumb.
Let us alone. What is it that will last?
All things are taken from us, and become
Portions and parcels of the dreadful past.
Let us alone. What pleasure can we have
To war with evil? Is there any peace
in ever climbing up the climbing wave?
All things have rest, and ripen toward the grave
In silence—ripen, fall and cease:
Give us long rest or death, dark death, or dreamful ease.

V

How sweet it were, hearing the downward stream,
With half-shut eyes ever to seem
Falling asleep in a half-dream!
To dream and dream, like yonder amber light,
Which will not leave the myrrh-bush on the height;
To hear each other's whispered speech;
Eating the Lotos day by day,
To watch the crisping ripples on the beach,
And tender curving lines of creamy spray;
To lend our hearts and spirits wholly
To the influence of mild-minded melancholy;
To muse and brood and live again in memory,
With those old faces of our infancy
Heaped over with a mound of grass,
Two handfuls of white dust, shut in an urn of brass!

VI

Dear is the memory of our wedded lives,
And dear the last embraces of our wives
And their warm tears: but all hath suffered change;
For surely now our household hearths are cold:
Our sons inherit us: our looks are strange:
And we should come like ghosts to trouble joy.
Or else the island princes over-bold
Have eat our substance, and the minstrel sings
Before them of the ten-years' war in Troy,
And our great deeds, as half-forgotten things.
Is there confusion in the little isle?
Let what is broken so remain.
The Gods are hard to reconcile:
'Tis hard to settle order once again.
There *is* confusion worse than death,
Trouble on trouble, pain on pain,
Long labor unto aged breath,
Sore tasks to hearts worn out with many wars
And eyes grown dim with gazing on the pilot-stars.

VII

But, propt on beds of amaranth and moly,
How sweet (while warm airs lull us, blowing lowly)

With half-dropped eyelid still,
Beneath a heaven dark and holy,
To watch the long bright river drawing slowly
His waters from the purple hill—
To hear the dewy echoes calling
From cave to cave through the thick-twined vine—
To watch the emerald-colored water falling
Through many a woven acanthus-wreath divine!
Only to hear and see the far-off sparkling brine,
Only to hear were sweet, stretched out beneath the pine.

VIII

The Lotos blooms below the barren peak:
The Lotos blows by every winding creek:
All day the wind breathes low with mellower tone:
Through every hollow cave and alley lone
Round and round the spicy downs the yellow Lotos dust is blown.
We have had enough of action, and of motion we,
Rolled to starboard, rolled to larboard, when the surge was seething free,
Where the wallowing monster spouted his foam-fountains in the sea.
Let us swear an oath, and keep it with an equal mind,
In the hollow Lotos-land to live and lie reclined
On the hills like Gods together, careless of mankind.
For they lie beside their nectar, and the bolts are hurled
Far below them in the valleys, and the clouds are lightly curled
Round their golden houses, girdled with the gleaming world:
Where they smile in secret, looking over wasted lands,
Blight and famine, plague and earthquake, roaring deeps and fiery sands,
Clanging fights, and flaming towns, and sinking ships, and praying hands.
But they smile, they find a music centered in a doleful song
Steaming up, a lamentation and an ancient tale of wrong,
Like a tale of little meaning though the words are strong;
Chanted from an ill-used race of men that cleave the soil,
Sow the seed, and reap the harvest with enduring toil,
Storing yearly little dues of wheat, and wine and oil;
Till they perish and they suffer—some, 'tis whispered—down in hell
Suffer endless anguish, others in Elysian valleys dwell,
Resting weary limbs at last on beds of asphodel.
Surely, surely, slumber is more sweet than toil, the shore
Than labor in the deep mid-ocean, wind and wave and oar;
O, rest ye, brother mariners, we will not wander more.

ULYSSES

ALFRED LORD TENNYSON

It little profits that an idle king,
By this still hearth, among these barren crags,
Matched with an aged wife, I mete and dole
Unequal laws unto a savage race,
That hoard, and sleep, and feed, and know not me.
I cannot rest from travel: I will drink
Life to the lees: all times I have enjoyed
Greatly, have suffered greatly, both with those
That loved me, and alone; on shore, and when
Through scudding drifts the rainy Hyades
Vext the dim sea. I am become a name;
For always roaming with a hungry heart
Much have I seen and known: cities of men
And manners, climates, councils, governments,
Myself not least, but honoured of them all,—
And drunk delight of battle with my peers,
Far on the ringing plains of windy Troy.
I am a part of all that I have met;
Yet all experience is an arch wherethrough
Gleams that untravelled world, whose margin fades
For ever and for ever when I move.
How dull it is to pause, to make an end,
To rust unburnished, not to shine in use!
As though to breathe were life. Life piled on life
Were all too little, and of one to me
Little remains: but every hour is saved
From that eternal silence, something more,
A bringer of new things; and vile it were

For some three suns to store and hoard myself,
And this gray spirit yearning in desire
To follow knowledge like a sinking star,
Beyond the utmost bound of human thought.
      This is my son, mine own Telemachus,
To whom I leave the scepter and the isle—
Well-loved of me, discerning to fulfill
This labor, by slow prudence to make mild
A rugged people, and through soft degrees
Subdue them to the useful and the good.
Most blameless is he, centered in the sphere
Of common duties, decent not to fail
In offices of tenderness, and pay
Meet adoration to my household gods,
When I am gone. He works his work, I mine.
      There lies the port: the vessel puffs her sail:
There gloom the dark, broad seas. My mariners,
Souls that have toiled, and wrought, and thought with me—
That ever with a frolic welcome took
The thunder and the sunshine, and opposed
Free hearts, free foreheads—you and I are old;
Old age hath yet his honour and his toil;
Death closes all: but something ere the end,
Some work of noble note, may yet be done,
Not unbecoming men that strove with Gods.
The lights begin to twinkle from the rocks:
The long day wanes: the slow moon climbs: the deep
Moans round with many voices. Come, my friends,
'Tis not too late to seek a newer world.
Push off, and sitting well in order smite
The sounding furrows; for my purpose holds
To sail beyond the sunset, and the baths
Of all the western stars, until I die.
It may be that the gulfs will wash us down:
It may be we shall touch the Happy Isles,
And see the great Achilles, whom we knew.
Though much is taken, much abides; and though
We are not now that strength which in old days
Moved earth and heaven, that which we are, we are,—
One equal temper of heroic hearts,
Made weak by time and fate, but strong in will
To strive, to seek, to find, and not to yield.

AB NEGATIVE
(THE SURGEON'S POEM)

BRIAN TURNER

Thalia Fields lies under a grey ceiling of clouds,
just under the turbulence, with anesthetics
dripping from an IV into her arm,
and the flight surgeon says *The shrapnel*
cauterized as it traveled through her
here, breaking this rib as it entered,
burning a hole through the left lung
to finish in her back, and all of this
she doesn't hear, except perhaps as music—
that faraway music of people's voices
when they speak gently and with care,
a comfort to her on a stretcher
in a flying hospital en route to Landstuhl,
just under the rain at midnight, and Thalia
drifts in and out of consciousness
as a nurse dabs her lips with a moist towel,
her palm on Thalia's forehead, her vitals
slipping some, as burned flesh gives way
to the heat of blood, the tunnels within
opening to fill her, just enough blood
to cough up and drown in; Thalia
sees shadows of people working
to save her, but cannot feel their hands,
cannot hear them any longer,
and when she closes her eyes
the most beautiful colors rise in darkness,

tangerine washing into Russian blue,
with the droning engine humming on
in a dragonfly's wings, island palms
painting the sky an impossible hue
with their thick brushes dripping green…
a way of dealing with the fact
that Thalia Fields is gone, long gone,
about as far from Mississippi
as she can get, ten thousand feet above Iraq
with a blanket draped over her body
and an exhausted surgeon in tears,
his bloodied hands on her chest, his head
sunk down, the nurse guiding him
to a nearby seat and holding him as he cries,
though no one hears it, because nothing can be heard
where pilots fly in blackout, the plane
like a shadow guiding the rain, here
in the droning engines of midnight.

OLD WAR-DREAMS

WALT WHITMAN

In midnight sleep of many a face of anguish,
Of the look at first of the mortally wounded, (of that
    indescribable look,)
Of the dead on their backs with arms extended wide,
       I dream, I dream, I dream.

Of scenes of Nature, fields and mountains,
Of skies so beauteous after a storm, and at night the moon
    so unearthly bright,
Shining sweetly, shining down, where we dig the trenches
    and gather the heaps,
       I dream, I dream, I dream.

Long have they pass'd, faces and trenches and fields,
Where through the carnage I moved with a callous
    composure, or away from the fallen,
Onward I sped at the time- but now of their forms at
    night,
       I dream, I dream, I dream.

THE USE OF FORCE

WILLIAM CARLOS WILLIAMS

They were new patients to me, all I had was the name, Olson. Please come down as soon as you can, my daughter is very sick.

When I arrived I was met by the mother, a big startled looking woman, very clean and apologetic who merely said, Is this the doctor? and let me in. In the back, she added. You must excuse us, doctor, we have her in the kitchen where it is warm. It is very damp here sometimes.

The child was fully dressed and sitting on her father's lap near the kitchen table. He tried to get up, but I motioned for him not to bother, took off my overcoat and started to look things over. I could see that they were all very nervous, eyeing me up and down distrustfully. As often, in such cases, they weren't telling me more than they had to, it was up to me to tell them; that's why they were spending three dollars on me.

The child was fairly eating me up with her cold, steady eyes, and no expression to her face whatever. She did not move and seemed, inwardly, quiet; an unusually attractive little thing, and as strong as a heifer in appearance. But her face was flushed, she was breathing rapidly, and I realized that she had a high fever. She had magnificent blonde hair, in profusion. One of those picture children often reproduced in advertising leaflets and the photogravure sections of the Sunday papers.

She's had a fever for three days, began the father and we don't know what it comes from. My wife has given her things, you know, like people do, but it don't do no good. And there's been a lot of sickness around. So we tho't you'd better look her over and tell us what is the matter.

As doctors often do I took a trial shot at it as a point of departure. Has she had a sore throat?

Both parents answered me together, No...No, she says her throat don't hurt her.

Does your throat hurt you? added the mother to the child. But the little girl's expression didn't change nor did she move her eyes from my face.

Have you looked?

I tried to, said the mother, but I couldn't see.

As it happens we had been having a number of cases of diphtheria in the school to which this child went during that month and we were all, quite apparently, thinking of that, though no one had as yet spoken of the thing.

Well, I said, suppose we take a look at the throat first. I smiled in my best professional manner and asking for the child's first name I said, come on, Mathilda, open your mouth and let's take a look at your throat.

Nothing doing.

Aw, come on, I coaxed, just open your mouth wide and let me take a look. Look, I said opening both hands wide, I haven't anything in my hands. Just open up and let me see.

Such a nice man, put in the mother. Look how kind he is to you. Come on, do what he tells you to. He won't hurt you.

At that I ground my teeth in disgust. If only they wouldn't use the word "hurt" I might be able to get somewhere. But I did not allow myself to be hurried or disturbed but speaking quietly and slowly I approached the child again.

As I moved my chair a little nearer suddenly with one catlike movement both her hands clawed instinctively for my eyes and she almost reached them too. In fact she knocked my glasses flying and they fell, though unbroken, several feet away from me on the kitchen floor.

Both the mother and father almost turned themselves inside out in embarrassment and apology. You bad girl, said the mother, taking her and shaking her by one arm. Look what you've done. The nice man...

For heaven's sake, I broke in. Don't call me a nice man to her. I'm here to look at her throat on the chance that she might have diphtheria and possibly die of it. But that's nothing to her. Look here, I said to the child, we're going to look at your throat. You're old enough to understand what I'm saying. Will you open it now by yourself or shall we have to open it for you?

Not a move. Even her expression hadn't changed. Her breaths however were coming faster and faster. Then the battle began. I had to do it. I had to have a throat culture for her own protection. But first I told the parents that it was entirely up to them. I explained the danger but said that I would not insist on a throat examination so long as they would take the responsibility.

If you don't do what the doctor says you'll have to go to the hospital, the mother admonished her severely.

Oh yeah? I had to smile to myself. After all, I had already fallen in love with the savage brat, the parents were contemptible to me. In the ensuing struggle they grew more and more abject, crushed, exhausted while she surely rose to magnificent heights of insane fury of effort bred of her terror of me.

The father tried his best, and he was a big man but the fact that she was his daughter, his shame at her behavior and his dread of hurting her made him release her just at the critical moment several times when I had almost achieved success, till I wanted to kill him. But his dread also that she might have diphtheria made him tell me to go on, go on though he himself was almost fainting, while the mother moved back and forth behind us raising and lowering her hands in an agony of apprehension.

Put her in front of you on your lap, I ordered, and hold both her wrists.

But as soon as he did the child let out a scream. Don't, you're hurting me. Let go of my hands. Let them go I tell you. Then she shrieked terrifyingly, hysterically. Stop it! Stop it! You're killing me!

Do you think she can stand it, doctor! said the mother.

You get out, said the husband to his wife. Do you want her to die of diphtheria?

Come on now, hold her, I said.

Then I grasped the child's head with my left hand and tried to get the wooden tongue depressor between her teeth. She fought, with clenched teeth, desperately! But now I also had grown furious—at a child. I tried to hold myself down but I couldn't. I know how to expose a throat for inspection. And I did my best. When finally I got the wooden spatula behind the last teeth and just the point of it into the mouth cavity, she opened up for an instant but before I could see anything she came down again and gripping the wooden blade between her molars she reduced it to splinters before I could get it out again.

Aren't you ashamed, the mother yelled at her. Aren't you ashamed to act like that in front of the doctor?

Get me a smooth-handled spoon of some sort, I told the mother. We're going through with this. The child's mouth was already bleeding. Her tongue was cut and she was screaming in wild hysterical shrieks. Perhaps I should have desisted and come back in an hour or more. No doubt it would have been better. But I have seen at least two children lying dead in bed of neglect in such cases, and feeling that I must get a diagnosis now or never I went at it again. But the worst of it was that I too had got beyond reason. I could have torn the child apart in my own fury and enjoyed it. It was a pleasure to attack her. My face was burning with it.

The damned little brat must be protected against her own idiocy, one says to one's self at such times. Others must be protected against her. It is a social necessity. And all these things are true. But a blind fury, a feeling of adult shame, bred of a longing for muscular release are the operatives. One goes on to the end.

In a final unreasoning assault I overpowered the child's neck and jaws. I forced the heavy silver spoon back of her teeth and down her throat till she gagged. And there it was—both tonsils covered with membrane. She had fought valiantly to keep me from knowing her secret. She had been hiding that sore throat for three days at least and lying to her parents in order to escape just such an outcome as this.

Now truly she *was* furious. She had been on the defensive before but now she attacked. Tried to get off her father's lap and fly at me while tears of defeat blinded her eyes.

THE GIRL
WITH A PIMPLY FACE

WILLIAM CARLOS WILLIAMS

One of the local druggists sent in the call: 50 Summer St., second floor, the door to the left. It's a baby they've just brought from the hospital. Pretty bad condition I should imagine. Do you want to make it? I think they've had somebody else but don't like him, he added as an afterthought.

It was half past twelve. I was just sitting down to lunch. Can't they wait till after office hours?

Oh I guess so. But they're foreigners and you know how they are. Make it as soon as you can. I guess the baby's pretty bad.

It was two-thirty when I got to the place, over a shop in the business part of town. One of those street doors between plate glass show windows. A narrow entry with smashed mail boxes on one side and a dark stair leading straight up. I'd been to the address a number of times during the past years to see various people who had lived there.

Going up I found no bell so I rapped vigorously on the wavy-glass door-panel to the left. I knew it to be the door to the kitchen, which occupied the rear of that apartment.

Come in, said a loud childish voice.

I opened the door and saw a lank haired girl of about fifteen standing chewing gum and eyeing me curiously from beside the kitchen table. The hair was coal black and one of her eyelids drooped a little as she spoke. Well, what do you want? she said. Boy, she was tough and no kidding but I fell for her immediately. There was that hard, straight thing about her that in itself gives an impression of excellence.

I'm the doctor, I said.

Oh, you're the doctor. The baby's inside. She looked at me. Want to see her?

Sure, that's what I came for. Where's your mother?

She's out. I don't know when she's coming back. But you can take a look at the baby if you want to.

All right. Let's see her.

She led the way into the bedroom, toward the front of the flat, one of the unlit rooms, the only windows being those in the kitchen and along the facade of the building.

There she is.

I looked on the bed and saw a small face, emaciated but quiet, unnaturally quiet, sticking out of the upper end of a tightly rolled bundle made by the rest of the baby encircled in a blue cotton blanket. The whole wasn't much larger than a good sized loaf of rye bread. Hands and everything were rolled up. Just the yellowish face showed, tightly hatted and framed around by a corner of the blanket.

What's the matter with her, I asked.

I dunno, said the girl as fresh as paint and seeming about as indifferent as though it had been no relative of hers instead of her sister. I looked at my informer very much amused and she looked back at me, chewing her gum vigorously, standing there her feet well apart. She cocked her head to one side and gave it to me straight in the eye, as much as to say, Well? I looked back at her. She had one of those small, squeezed up faces, snub nose, overhanging eyebrows, low brow and a terrible complexion, pimply and coarse.

When's your mother coming back do you *think,* I asked again.

Maybe in an hour. But maybe you'd better come some time when my father's here. He talks English. He ought to come in around five I guess.

But can't you tell me something about the baby? I hear it's been sick. Does it have a fever?

I dunno.

But has it diarrhoea, are its movements green?

Sure, she said, I guess so. It's been in the hospital but it got worse so my father brought it home today.

What are they feeding it?

A bottle. You can see that yourself. There it is.

There was a cold bottle of half finished milk lying on the coverlet the nipple end of it fallen behind the baby's head.

How old is she? It's girl, did you say?

Yeah, it's a girl.

Your sister?

Sure. Want to examine it?

No thanks, I said. For the moment at least I had lost all interest in the baby. This young kid in charge of the house did something to me that I liked. She was just a child but nobody was putting anything over on her if she knew it, yet the real thing about her was the complete lack of the rotten smell of a liar. She wasn't in the least presumptive. Just straight.

But after all she wasn't such a child. She had breasts you knew would be like small stones to the hand, good muscular arms and fine hard legs. Her bare feet were stuck into broken down sandals such as you see worn by children at the beach in summer. She was heavily tanned too, wherever her skin showed. Just one of the kids you'll find loafing around the pools they have outside towns and cities everywhere these days. A tough little nut finding her own way in the world.

What's the matter with your legs? I asked. They were bare and covered with scabby sores.

Poison ivy, she answered, pulling up her skirts to show me.

Gee, but you ought to seen it two days ago. This ain't nothing. You're a doctor. What can I do for it?

Let's see, I said.

She put her leg up on a chair. It had been badly bitten by mosquitoes, as I saw the thing, but she insisted on poison ivy. She had torn at the affected places with her finger nails and that's what made it look worse.

Oh that's not so bad, I said, if you'll only leave it alone and stop scratching it.

Yeah, I know that but I can't. Scratching's the only thing makes it feel better.

What's that on your foot?

Where? Looking.

That big brown spot there on the back of your foot.

Dirt I guess. Her gum chewing never stopped and her fixed defensive non-expression never changed.

Why don't you wash it?

I do. Say, what could I do for my face?

I looked at it closely. You have what they call acne, I told her. All those blackheads and pimples you see there, well, let's see, the first thing you ought to do, I suppose, is to get some good soap.

What kind of soap? Lifebuoy?

No. I'd suggest one of those cakes of Lux. Not the flakes but the cake.

Yeah, I know, she said. Three for seventeen.

Use it. Use it every morning. Bathe your face in very hot water. You know, until the skin is red from it. That's to bring the blood up to the skin. Then take a piece of ice. You have ice, haven't you?

Sure, we have ice.

Hold it in a face cloth—or whatever you have—and rub that all over your face. Do that right after you've washed it in the very hot water—before it has cooled. Rub the ice all over. And do it every day—for a month. Your skin will improve. If you like, you can take some cold cream once in a while, not much, just a little and rub that in last of all, if your face feels too dry.

Will that help me?

If you stick to it, it'll help you.

All right.

There's a lotion I could give you to use along with that. Remind me of it when I come back later. Why aren't you in school?

Agh, I'm not going any more. They can't make me. Can they?

They can try.

How can they? I know a girl thirteen that don't go and they can't make her either.

Don't you want to learn things?

I know enough already.

Going to get a job?

I got a job. Here. I been helping the Jews across the hall. They give me three fifty a week—all summer.

Good for you, I said. Think your father'll be here around five?

Guess so. He ought to be.

I'll come back then. Make it all the same call.

All right, she said, looking straight at me and chewing her gum as vigorously as ever.

Just then a little blond haired thing of about seven came in through the kitchen and walked to me looking curiously at my satchel and then at the baby.

What are you, a doctor?

See you later, I said to the older girl and went out.

At five-thirty I once more climbed the wooden stairs after passing two women at the street entrance who looked me up and down from where they were leaning on the brick wall of the building talking.

This time a woman's voice said, Come in, when I knocked on the kitchen door.

It was the mother. She was impressive, a bulky woman, growing toward fifty, in a black dress, with lank graying hair and a long seamed face. She stood by the enameled kitchen table. A younger, plumpish woman with blond hair, well cared for and in a neat house dress—as if she had dolled herself up for the occasion—was standing beside her. The small blank child was there too and the older girl, behind the others, overshadowed by her mother, the two older women at least a head taller than she. No one spoke.

Hello, I said to the girl I had been talking to earlier. She didn't answer me.

Doctor, began the mother, save my baby. She very sick. The woman spoke with a thick, heavy voice and seemed overcome with grief and apprehension. Doctor! Doctor! She all but wept.

All right, I said to cut the woman short, let's take a look at her first.

So everybody headed toward the front of the house, the mother in the lead. As they went I lagged behind to speak to the second woman, the interpreter. What happened?

The baby was not doing so well. So they took it to the hospital to see if the doctors there could help it. But it got worse. So her husband took it out this morning. It looks bad to me.

Yes, said the mother who had overheard us. Me got seven children. One daughter married. This my baby, pointing to the child on the bed. And she wiped her face with the back of her hand. This baby no do good. Me almost crazy. Don't know who can help. What doctor, I don't know. Somebody tell me take to hospital. I think maybe do some good. Five days she there. Cost me two dollar every day. Ten dollar. I no got money. And when I see my baby, she worse. She look dead. I can't leave she there. No. No. I say to everybody, no. I take she home. Doctor, you save my baby. I pay you. I pay you everything—

Wait a minute, wait a minute, I said. Then I turned to the other woman. What happened?

The baby got like a diarrhoea in the hospital. And she was all dirty when they went to see her. They got all excited—

All sore behind, broke in the mother—

The younger woman said a few words to her in some language that sounded like Russian but it didn't stop her—

No. No. I send she to hospital. And when I see my baby like that I can't leave she there. My babies no that way. Never, she emphasized. Never! I take she home.

Take your time, I said. Take off her clothes. Everything off. This is a regular party. It's warm enough in here. Does she vomit?

She no eat. How she can vomit? said the mother.

But the other woman contradicted her. Yes, she was vomiting in the hospital, the nurse said.

It happens that this September we had been having a lot of such cases in my hospital also, an infectious diarrhoea which practically all the children got when they came in from any cause. I supposed that this was what happened to this child. No doubt it had been in a bad way before that, improper feeding, etc., etc. And then when they took it in there, for whatever had been the matter with it, the diarrhoea had developed. These things sometimes don't turn out so well. Lucky, no doubt, that they had brought it home when they did. I told them so, explaining at the same time: One nurse for ten or twenty babies, they do all they can but you can't run and change the whole ward every five minutes. But the infant looked too lifeless for that only to be the matter with it.

You want all clothes off, asked the mother again, hesitating and trying to keep the baby covered with the cotton blanket while undressing it.

Everything off, I said.

There it lay, just skin and bones with a round fleshless head at the top and the usual pot belly you find in such cases.

Look, said the mother, tilting the infant over on its right side with her big hands so that I might see the reddened buttocks. What kind of nurse that. My babies never that way.

Take you time, take your time, I told her. That's not bad. And it wasn't either. Any child with loose movements might have had the same half an hour after being cared for. Come on. Move away, I said and give me a chance. She kept hovering over the baby as if afraid I might expose it.

It had no temperature. There was no rash. The mouth was in reasonably good shape. Eyes, ears negative. The moment I put my stethoscope to the little boney chest, however, the whole thing became clear. The infant had a severe congenital heart defect, a roar when you listened over the heart that meant, to put it crudely, that she was no good, never would be.

The mother was watching me. I straightened up and looking at her told her plainly: She's got a bad heart.

That was the sign for tears. The big woman cried while she spoke. Doctor, she pleaded in blubbering anguish, save my baby.

I'll help her, I said, but she's got a bad heart. That will never be any better. But I knew perfectly well she wouldn't pay the least attention to what I was saying.

I give you anything, she went on. I pay you. I pay you twenty dollar. Doctor, you fix my baby. You good doctor. You fix.

All right, all right, I said. What are you feeding it?

They told me and it was a ridiculous formula, unboiled besides. I regulated it properly for them and told them how to proceed to make it up. Have you got enough bottles, I asked the young girl.

Sure, we got bottles, she told me.

O.K., then go ahead.

You think you cure she? The mother with her long, tearful face was at me again, so different from her tough female fifteen-year-old.

You do what I tell you for three days, I said, and I'll come back and see how you're getting on.

Tank you, doctor, so much. I pay you. I got today no money. I pay ten dollar to hospital. They cheat me. I got no more money. I pay you Friday when my husband get pay. You save my baby.

Boy! what a woman. I couldn't get away.

She my baby, doctor. I no want to lose. Me got seven children—

Yes, you told me.

But this my baby. You understand. She very sick. You good doctor—

Oh my God! To get away from her I turned again to the kid. You better get going after more bottles before the stores close. I'll come back Friday morning.

How about that stuff for my face you were gonna give me.

That's right. Wait a minute. And I sat down on the edge of the bed to write out a prescription for some lotio alba comp. such as we use in acne. The two older women looked at me in astonishment—wondering, I suppose, how I knew the girl. I finished writing the thing and handed it to her. Sop it on your face at bedtime, I said, and let it dry on. Don't get it in your eyes.

No, I won't.

I'll see you in a couple of days, I said to them all.

Doctor! The old woman was still after me. You come back. I pay you. But all a time short. Always tomorrow come milk man. Must pay rent, must pay coal. And no got money. Too much work. Too much wash. Too much cook. Nobody help. I don't know what's a matter. This door, doctor, this door. This house make me sick. Make sick.

Do the best I can, I said as I was leaving.

The girl followed on the stairs. How much is this going to cost, she asked shrewdly holding the prescription.

Not much, I said, and then started to think. Tell them you only got half a dollar. Tell them I said that's all it's worth.

Is that right, she said.

Absolutely. Don't pay a cent more for it.

Say, you're all right, she looked at me appreciatively.

Have you got half a dollar?

Sure. Why not.

What's it all about, my wife asked me in the evening. She had heard about the case. Gee! I sure met a wonderful girl, I told her.

What! another?

Some tough baby. I'm crazy about her. Talk about straight stuff…And I recounted to her the sort of case it was and what I had done. The mother's an odd one too. I don't quite make her out.

Did they pay you?

No. I don't suppose they have any cash.

Going back?

Sure. Have to.

Well, I don't see why you have to do all this charity work. Now that's a case you should report to the Emergency Relief. You'll get at least two dollars a call from them.

But the father has a job, I understand. That counts me out.

What sort of a job?

I dunno. Forgot to ask.

What's the baby's name so I can put it in the book?

Damn it. I never thought to ask them that either. I think they must have told me but I can't remember it. Some kind of a Russian name—

You're the limit. Dumbbell, she laughed. Honestly—Who are they anyhow?

You know, I think it must be that family Kate was telling us about. Don't you remember. The time the little kid was playing there one afternoon after school, fell down the front steps and knocked herself senseless.

I don't recall.

Sure you do. That's the family. I get it now. Kate took the brat down there in a taxi and went up with her to see that everything was all right. Yop, that's it. The old woman took the older kid by the hair, because she hadn't watched her sister. And what a beating she gave her. Don't you remember Kate telling us afterward. She thought the old woman was going to murder the child she screamed and threw her around so. Some old gal. You can see they're all afraid of her. What a world. I suppose the damned brat drives her cuckoo. But boy, how she clings to that baby.

The last hope, I suppose, said my wife.

Yeah, and the worst bet in the lot. There's a break for you.

She'll love it just the same.

More, usually.

Three days later I called at the flat again. Come in. This time a resonant male voice. I entered, keenly interested.

By the same kitchen table stood a short, thickset man in baggy working pants and a heavy cotton undershirt. He seemed to have the stability of a cube placed on one of its facets, a smooth highly colored Slavic face, long black moustaches and widely separated, perfectly candid blue eyes. His black hair, glossy and profuse stood out carelessly all over his large round head. By his look he reminded me at once of his blond haired daughter, absolutely unruffled. The shoulders of an ox. You the doctor, he said. Come in.

The girl and the small child were beside him, the mother was in the bedroom.

The baby no better. Won't eat, said the man in answer to my first question.

How are its bowels?

Not so bad.

Does it vomit?

No.

Then it is better, I objected. But by this time the mother had heard us talking and came in. She seemed worse than the last time. Absolutely inconsolable. Doctor! Doctor! She came up to me.

Somewhat irritated I put her aside and went in to the baby. Of course it was much better, much better. So I told them. But the heart, naturally, was the same.

How she heart? the mother pressed me eagerly. Today little better?

I started to explain things to the man who was standing back giving his wife precedence but as soon as she got the drift of what I was saying she was all over me again and the tears began to pour. There was no use my talking. Doctor, you good doctor. You do something fix my baby. And before I could move she took my left hand in both hers and kissed it through her tears. As she did so I realized finally that she had been drinking.

I turned toward the man, looking a good bit like the sun at noonday and as indifferent, then back to the woman and I felt deeply sorry for her.

Then, not knowing why I said it nor of whom, precisely I was speaking, I felt myself choking inwardly with the words: Hell! God damn it. The sons of bitches. Why do these things have to be?

The next morning as I came into the coat room at the hospital there were several of the visiting staff standing there with their cigarettes, talking. It was about a hunting dog belonging to one of the doctors. It had come down with distemper and seemed likely to die.

I called up half a dozen vets around here, one of them was saying. I even called up the one in your town, he added turning to me as I came in. And do you know how much they wanted to charge me for giving the serum to that animal?

Nobody answered.

They had the nerve to want to charge me five dollars a shot for it. Can you beat that? Five dollars a shot.

Did you give them the job, someone spoke up facetiously.

Did I? I should say I did not, the first answered. But can you beat that. Why we're nothing but a lot of slop-heels compared to those guys. We deserve to starve.

Get it out of them, someone rasped, kidding. That's the stuff.

Then the original speaker went on, buttonholing me as some of the others faded from the room. Did you ever see practice so rotten. By the way, I was called over to your town about a week ago to see a kid I delivered up here during the summer. Do you know anything about the case?

I probably got them on my list, I said. Russians?

Yeah, I thought as much. Has a job as a road worker or something. Said they couldn't pay me. Well, I took the trouble of going up to your court house and finding out what he was getting. Eighteen dollars a week. Just the type. And they had the nerve to tell me they couldn't pay me.

She told me ten.

She's a liar.

Natural maternal instinct, I guess.

Whisky appetite, if you should ask me.

Same thing.

O.K., buddy. Only I'm telling you. And did I tell *them*. They'll never call me down there again, believe me. I had that much satisfaction out of them anyway. You make 'em pay you. Don't you do anything for them unless they do. He's paid by the county. I tell you if I had taxes to pay down there I'd go and take it out of his salary.

You and how many others?

Say, they're bad actors, that crew. Do you know what they really do with their money? Whisky. Now I'm telling you. That old woman is the slickest customer you ever saw. She's drunk all the time. Didn't you notice it?

Not while I was there.

Don't you let them put any of that sympathy game over on you. Why they tell me she leaves that baby lying on the bed all day long screaming its lungs out until the neighbors complain to the police about it. I'm not lying to you.

Yeah, the old skate's got nerves, you can see that. I can imagine she's a bugger when she gets going.

But what about the young girl, I asked weakly. She seems like a pretty straight kid.

My confrere let out a wild howl. That thing! You mean that pimply faced little bitch. Say, if I had my way I'd run her out of the town tomorrow morning. There's about a dozen wise guys on her trail every night in the week. Ask the cops. Just ask them. They know. Only nobody wants to bring in a complaint. They say you'll stumble over her on the roof, behind the stairs anytime at all. Boy, they sure took you in.

Yes, I suppose they did, I said.

But the old woman's the ringleader. She's got the brains. Take my advice and make them pay.

The last time I went I heard the, Come In! from the front of the house. The fifteen-year-old was in there at the window in a rocking chair with the tightly wrapped baby in her arms. She got up. Her legs were bare to the hips. A powerful little animal.

What are you doing? Going swimming? I asked.

Naw, that's my gym suit. What the kids wear for Physical Training in school.

How's the baby?

She's all right.

Do you mean it?

Sure, she eats fine now.

Tell your mother to bring it to the office some day so I can weigh it. The food'll need increasing in another week or two anyway.

I'll tell her.

How's your face?

Gettin' better.

My God, it *is,* I said. And it was much better. Going back to school now?

Yeah, I had tuh.

Any description of essential works too long to include in this anthology must begin with Homer's epics, the *Iliad* and the *Odyssey*. The *Odyssey* is our greatest story of **homecoming** from battle, and the *Iliad* is not only our foundational account of men at war, but is also a sustained contemplation of **anger**. In Robert Fagles's excellent and lively translation, "rage" is indeed the first word.

The number of other important longer works that reference these two masterpieces underlines their seminal character. Pairing Homer's poems, in whole or in part, with any of these major reworkings can lead to rewarding discussions. Contemporary psychiatrist Jonathan Shay's two books about his work with Viet Nam veterans demonstrate the continuing relevance of these ancient Greek epics to our understanding of modern war and its costs to our warriors. Both his *Odysseus in America: Combat Trauma and the Trials of Homecoming* and his *Achilles in Vietnam* weave together contemporary experience and stories almost three thousand years old to illuminate issues of **trauma and recovery, anger and betrayal,** and **difficulties of homecoming**.

The protagonist of Peter Pouncey's recent novel, *Rules for Old Men Waiting*, often refers to Homer in order to explore his own experience in World War II, his son's death in Viet Nam, and his work as a historian with victims of World War I gas attacks. Refusing help from the health care system, the terminally ill MacIver chooses to die alone, but, seeking to come to terms with his own **anger**, not before he has composed his own war story. This brief work also raises issues of **aging** and the **power of story**.

Unfortunately out of print, Marilyn Nelson's anthology, *Rumors of Troy: Poems Inspired by The Iliad*, is available on Amazon and other markets for used books. Some poems in this collection of thirty-eight modern works respond to specific passages from the epic; these might be paired with those excerpts, allowing readers to sample Homer's majesty in small doses. Nelson was commissioned by the US Military Academy at West Point to produce this anthology for use in its English courses. Her own poems about her father's service in the Tuskegee Airmen, the corps of pioneering African American pilots, appear in this reader.

Produced approximately three hundred years after Homer, *Philoctetes* records another central tale of the Trojan War. This ancient Greek tragedy by Sophocles turns on the **anger** a warrior feels when he is **betrayed** by his own comrades. Unable to bear the stench of his wound and the horror of his cries, the Greeks have abandoned Philoctetes on a deserted island. They later learn they must convince this alienated archer to return and fight for them if they are ever to take Troy. Philoctetes will also be healed—but only if he reintegrates himself into the very community by which he feels betrayed. A moving account of physical **pain**, this play explores both the compassion and the revulsion others may feel for the wounded body. The modern critic Edmund Wilson in *The Wound and the Bow* saw this play as embodying one of our great myths: the possible connection between our wounds and our powerful gifts.

Like "Winthrop Cohen" in this anthology, Pat Barker's World War I trilogy, *Regeneration, The Eye in the Door,* and *Ghost Road,* explores the ethical dilemmas mental health professionals face in treating battlefield **trauma**. The novels imagine the experience of William Rivers, the famous psychiatrist and anthropologist who treated many victims of "shell shock" during World War I, including some of the poets—Wilfred Owen and Sigfried Sassoon—who served in that war. Their work would of course be a wonderful complement to this anthology, and there is a very inexpensive collection available, *World War One British Poets* published by Dover. Rebecca West's first novel, *The Return of the Soldier,* explores similar dilemmas in a short, apparently simple account of a **homecoming** of a "shell shocked" soldier to an estate outside London, where, even as the Great War and familial loss are taking their toll, the inhabitants strive for a measured, outwardly exquisite existence.

March, by Geraldine Brooks, revisits Louisa May Alcott's domestic novel, *Little Women.* Largely absent from the nineteenth-century classic, the father who is away serving as a chaplain in the Civil War becomes the central figure in Brooks' contemporary retelling. March's letters home clearly "protect" his wife and daughters from the realities of the battlefield, but his inability either to share his experience with them or to come to terms with it himself reveals the tensions that make **homecoming** so difficult in all wars. Moreover, the second part of the novel, in which Marmee travels to a hospital in Washington D.C. to help care for her seriously ill husband, challenges any sense that the domestic sphere is "trivial" compared with the experience of war. It also reminds us that families may have their own reasons for finding it difficult to reconnect with returning soldiers. Brooks, a journalist who covered the Middle East, claims that this historical novel "was written against the tumult of my own feelings about the war with Iraq." Her account of conditions in Civil War hospitals for the sick and wounded is informed by Louisa May Alcott's own book about her work as a volunteer in such a hospital, *Civil War Hospital Sketches.* Combining *March* with selections from *Little Women* and from *Hospital Sketches* can make for a particularly rich discussion. This work also provokes thinking about **racism** and the **trauma** of failing to live up to one's own ideals under wartime circumstances.

The caregiving of families and the hard work of reconnecting with a loved one who comes home changed are also central to Cathy Crimmins's *Where Is the Mango Princess?: A Journey Back from Brain Injury.* Crimmins's story of her husband's partial recovery from **traumatic brain injury** following a boating accident educates readers about one of the most common injuries among soldiers returning from Iraq. Carefully researched, the memoir also evokes what it feels like to be, or to live with, a brain-injured person. Originally a humorist, Crimmins raises questions about **black humor** as a response to tragedy in a way that resonates with many health care providers. Honest about the difficulties as well as the rewards of caring for a man whose personality and capabilities have forever changed, Crimmins's study of traumatic brain injury deals with the essential issues of loyalty, and of balancing needs in a family, that are involved in living with a **chronic condition**.

"Reynolds Price is dead. Who will you be now? Who can you be and how can you get there, double-time?" In his memoir *A Whole New Life,* the novelist and poet claims speaking these harsh words would have been "the kindest thing anyone could have done for me" after he received radiation for the malignant spinal tumor that ultimately left him a paraplegic. Readers may find Price's views controversial, but he covers an astonishing range of topics pertinent to anyone needing to reinvent the self after life-changing illness or injury: the effect of illness on his sexuality; his spiritual life and the visions of Jesus that sustained him; specific tips for dealing with continence issues and urinary tract infections. Price's years-long search for therapies to resolve chronic **pain** are illuminating. He is particularly unsparing in his call for doctors to treat patients with basic humanity as well as with technical skill. Those who care for veterans should find much to talk about in this eloquent memoir of adjusting to and living with a **chronic condition**.

Gregor Samsa's transformation into an insect might seem to have little to do with more common medical problems, but the alienation embodied in the hero of Franz Kafka's *Metamorphosis* prompts surprising comparisons with the feelings of some returning veterans. Moreover, this bizarre tale turns on pragmatic issues such as **poverty** and **unemployment**. Gregor's attempts to renegotiate both his own **sense of identity** and his place in his family after a profound change echo problems of **homecoming**. Garrett's "Wounded Soldier (Cartoon Strip)" in this anthology raises many of the same issues.

Leslie Marmon Silko's 1977 novel *Ceremony* examines ways that **cultural traditions** may influence healing. Returning to the Laguna Pueblo reservation after service in World War II, Tayo's **trauma** and coming to terms with killing are complicated, and ultimately resolved, by Native American beliefs. The flashbacks he experiences will be familiar to most people who work with soldiers, but the specific rituals that help resolve his alienation may be less so. Tayo himself feels failed by the Army doctor who tells him "No Indian medicine." Accepted as a soldier in uniform, Tayo finds his **homecoming** tainted by **racism**. Similarly the **substance abuse** used as self-medication by some veterans is complicated here by the complex history of alcohol on Native American reservations. This beautifully written book celebrates the common **power of story** to help warriors recover and return to their communities, but it does so within a specifically Native American tradition.

Inconsistent **cultural traditions** are the most obvious subject of *The Spirit Catches You and You Fall Down: A Hmong Child, Her American Doctors, and the Collision of Two Cultures.* However, as we discovered when we considered excerpting parts of Anne Fadiman's case study of an epileptic child living in Merced, California, the most important achievement of this long book may be to convince us that we cannot understand anything if we omit any perspective or what seem at first to be irrelevant, "non-medical" facts. Among the most important works about medicine in the past twenty years, this is essential reading not only in every VA, but in every hospital—and most readers find it a page-turner.

Ernest Hemingway's collection of linked short stories, *In Our Time,* contains pieces that should reward reading in any hospital. "Indian Camp" raises questions about differing **cultural traditions** and how these might affect the balance between **empathy and professional detachment** in the practice of medicine. Hemingway splices vignettes from World War I and the Greco-Turkish War with stories about a young boy's coming of age, thus linking wartime atrocities with initiation into life's other nearly unbearable realities. "Soldier's Home" distills a veteran's overwhelming **anger** and alienation from his family into a few brief incidents. Another account of **homecoming**, the lengthy "Big Two-Hearted River," is famous as an account of **trauma** that never mentions the war. Perhaps beginning to heal himself through a solitary fishing trip into a beautiful but also damaged natural world, the fragile and depressed man in this story reveals the severity of his psychic wounds only by his constant, careful self-management.

Dispatches is a book that can help health care providers begin to get inside the experience of soldiers at war. The author, Michael Herr, had been a film reviewer before *Esquire* sent him to Viet Nam to write about Saigon in 1967, and *Dispatches,* published ten years later, is filled with cinematic images of war. His writing captures the hallucinogenic quality of night patrols fueled by Dexedrine, the rot of the jungle and the fear of an enemy who was everywhere but rarely where you could see him. It is about the courage and compassion of the troops, their fears and despair, their comaraderie and their nightmares. It is also about Herr's role as an observer who cannot be objective because he cares too much about these men, and, like Hemingway and Stephen Crane, Herr makes us care too: these are our nephews and the neighbors' kids; we knew them just last year when they were in high school. While Herr is a journalist, health care providers too will understand this tension between **empathy and professional detachment**.

Tim O'Brien's *The Things They Carried* also conveys the sensations of serving in Viet Nam. In addition, this series of linked short stories employs memories and flashbacks to reflect on that experience and its relationship, or lack of it, to soldiers' previous lives at home. The title story is particularly recommended, as is "The Lives of the Dead." "The Man I Killed" might be paired with Hardy's "The Man He Killed" in this anthology to discuss **coming to terms with killing**.

Larry Brown's *Dirty Work* is about two devastatingly wounded Viet Nam vets from the South, one black and one white. Lying side by side in a veteran's hospital, they talk about combat, movies, sex, old loves, their boyhoods, how it feels to kill a man and why God allows wars to happen, taking the reader from the experience (and horrors) of war to the battle presented by their present condition—questioning their **sense of identity**, as well as several other relevant issues.

Finally, Helen Benedict received the James Aronson Award for Social Justice Journalism in 2008 for her article, "The Private War of Women Soldiers," in the March 2007 *Salon*. Her book on **sexual assault** in the military, *The Lonely Soldier: The Private War of Women Soldiers,* has just appeared in 2009. Dr. Mic Hunter's *Honor Betrayed: Sexual Abuse in America's Military* makes it clear that men can also be victims.

NOTES ON AUTHORS

Anne Brashler (b. 1924)   "He Read to Her"   7

Anne Brashler is the author of two collections—one of short stories, Getting Jesus in the Mood; *and one of poetry,* The Talking Poems. *Her work, both stories and poems, has appeared in many literary magazines, including* The Transatlantic Review, Confrontations, Other Voices, New Letters, Whetstone *and* The River Oak Review. *A resident of Illinois, Brashler is a former Writer in Residence for the Illinois Arts Council, and the editer of 17 years of* Story Quarterly.

Raymond Carver (1939 – 1988)   "Where I'm Calling From"   10

Raymond Carver, poet and master of the short story, was born in Oregon and lived in Port Angeles, Washington, most of his life. He was the recipient of many fellowships and awards, including the prestigious Mildred and Harold Strauss Living Award and Poetry *magazine's Levinson Prize. He was also a member of the American Academy of Arts and Letters.*

Wanda Coleman (b. 1946)   "Slave Driver"   22

Born in the Watts section of Los Angeles, Wanda Coleman is an award-winning author of poetry and short stories, focused particularly on themes of racism and the female experience. She published her first poems in a local newspaper at the age of 13, and has since worked as an editor, medical secretary, waitress, drama writer and a Peace Corps/Vista recruiter.

Andre Dubus (1936 – 1999)   "Out of the Snow"   28
                                      "Dancing After Hours"   40

Born in Lake Charles, Louisiana, Andre Dubus was taught by the Christian Brothers, and, after college, joined the Marines. After five and a half years in the service, Dubus enrolled in the Iowa Writer's Workshop and received a Master's in Fine Arts from the University of Iowa. In 1966, Dubus and his young family moved to Massachusetts, where he remained, teaching and writing until the end of his life.

Louise Erdrich (b. 1954)   "The Red Convertible"   63

Louise Erdrich was born to a German-American father and a French and Anishinaabe (Ojibwa) mother, and grew up in North Dakota, where her parents taught at the Bureau of Indian Affairs school. She earned a BA degree at Dartmouth College, where she met her future husband, the Modoc anthropologist and writer Michael Dorris, who was then director of the college's Native American Studies program. Erdrich received an MA in creative writing from Johns Hopkins University in 1979, and in 1982 her story "The World's Greatest Fisherman" was awarded the $5,000 Nelson Algren Prize for short fiction. In 1984, Erdrich published Love Medicine, *which includes an early version of "The Red Convertible." It was awarded the 1984 National Book Critics Circle Award.*

Robert Frost (1874 – 1963)   "Desert Places"   71
                                                         "An Old Man's Winter Night"   72

Born in San Francisco, Frost moved to New England at the age of eleven. He was enrolled at Dartmouth College, and later at Harvard, though he never earned a formal degree. After his New Hampshire farm failed, Frost moved to England where he met and was influenced by British poets as well as Ezra Pound. By the time he returned to the United States in 1915, he had published two full-length collections, and his reputation was established. By the 1920s, he was the most celebrated poet in America, and with each new book his fame and honors (including four Pulitzer Prizes) increased. He became a national celebrity, our nearly official Poet Laureate, and a great performer in the tradition of that earlier master of the literary vernacular, Mark Twain.

Mavis Gallant (b. 1922)   "My Heart is Broken"   73

Born in Montreal, Canada, Mavis Gallant has lived most of her adult life in France. Her writing career began in journalism, but she later turned to fiction. Today her work, including essays, short stories and reviews, appears in periodicals such as The New Yorker, The New York Times Book Review, *and* The New Republic.

George Palmer Garrett, Jr. (1929 – 2008)   "Wounded Soldier (Cartoon Strip)"   79

A poet and novelist, Gallant was the poet laureate of Virginia from 2002 to 2006. His novels include The Finished Man, Double Vision, *and the Elizabethan Trilogy, composed of* Death of the Fox, The Succession, *and* Entered from the Sun. *Garrett taught at Hollins College and, for many years, the University of Virginia. From 1952 to 1955 he served in the United States Army Field Artillery.*

Atul Gawande, MD (b. 1965)   "Casualties of War"   86
                                                             "The Way We Age Now"   96

Atul Gawande, a 2006 MacArthur Fellow, was born in Brooklyn, New York to physician parents. He is a general surgeon at the Brigham and Women's Hospital in Boston, a staff writer for The New Yorker *and an assistant professor at Harvard Medical School and Harvard School of Public Health, from which he earned his MD and MPH, respectively. His first book,* Complications: A Surgeon's Notes on an Imperfect Science, *was a 2002 National Book Award finalist and a best seller.*

Thomas Hardy (1840 – 1927)   "The Man He Killed"   110

Novelist, poet and short story writer, Thomas Hardy was born in Dorset, England. During his lifetime, he wrote almost a thousand published poems and fourteen published novels. In 1910 the King awarded him the Order of Merit for distinguished service in literature. Upon his death, his ashes were buried in Poet's Corner, Westminster Abbey, and his heart (literally) in Dorset with his first wife.

Arthur Kleinman, MD (b. 1941) "Winthrop Cohen" 111

An anthropologist and psychiatrist, Arthur Kleinman draws upon a bicultural, multidisciplinary background to propose alternative strategies for thinking about how the social and medical relate. Kleinman is Professor of Anthropology, Harvard University, and Presley Professor of Medical Anthropology and Chair of Social Medicine at Harvard Medical School. He is the author of many books, including Patients and Healers in the Context of Culture, Social Origins of Distress and Disease *and* The Illness Narrative, Culture and Depression *and more recently,* What Really Matters: Living a Moral Life Amidst Uncertainty and Danger.

Richard Lovelace (1618 – 1657) "To Lucasta, on Going to the Wars" 118

Born to a distinguished military family, English poet Richard Lovelace was educated at Oxford. He served as a captain in the Bishop Wars, and later engaged in political activism that sent him to prison twice. His experiences inspired his almost 200 poems.

Nancy Mairs (b. 1943) "On Being a Cripple" 119

A poet and essayist, Nancy Mairs is known for her personal voice on issues of social justice, spirituality and feminism. She earned her AB at Wheaton College, which awarded her a Doctor of Humane Letters thirty years later. She received her MFA in creative writing (poetry) and a PhD in English literature from the University of Arizona. She has been a high school teacher and university professor and lives in Tucson, Arizona.

Veneta Masson (b. 1944) "The Promise" 129

A nurse in practice for thirty-five years, twenty of them in primary health care, Veneta Masson was a founder, director and family nurse practitioner in a small clinic providing office and home care to an inner-city neighborhood in Washington, D.C. She is the author of Ninth Street Notebook—Voice of a Nurse in the City, *a collection of short pieces about major issues in health care from the front lines,* Rehab at the Florida Avenue Grill, *a collection of poems about events and people whose lives changed hers, and most recently,* Clinician's Guide to the Soul.

Marilyn Nelson (b. 1946) "Star-Fix" 131
"Freeman Field" 134
"Three Men in a Tent" 137
"Porter" 141

The daughter of a U.S. serviceman and a teacher, poet Marilyn Nelson was raised on military bases. She holds a BA from the University of California and postgraduate degrees from the University of Pennsylvania (MA) and the University of Minnesota (PhD). She retired as a professor of English after 30 years at the University of Connecticut. This former Poet Laureate of Connecticut is the founder and director of Soul Mountain Retreat, which offers residencies to writers.

Frank O'Connor (1903 – 1966)   "My Oedipus Complex"   144

Raised in Ireland, O'Connor's early life was marked by his father's alcoholism, indebtedness and ill-treatment of his mother. As a young man he joined in the Irish Republican Army's resistance to British rule, and his opposition to the Anglo-Irish Treaty of 1921 led to his imprisonment between 1922 and 1923. Following his release, O'Connor was a teacher, theatre director, and librarian. In 1935, he joined the Board of Directors of the Abbey Theatre in Dublin, founded by William Butler Yeats and other members of the Irish National Theatre Society, later becoming managing director for two years. Beginning in 1950, O'Connor began to accept invitations to teach in the United States, where many of his short stories had been published in The New Yorker *to great acclaim.*

Dorothy Parker (1893 – 1967)   "War Song"   153

Writer and poet Dorothy Parker was best known for her caustic wit, wisecracks, and sharp eye for 20th century urban foibles. Parker was well known as a frequent contributor to The New Yorker *and as a founding member of the famous Algonquin Round Table. Following the demise of that circle, Parker went to Hollywood, where she became a successful screenwriter and was nominated twice for an Academy Award. Blacklisted because of her involvement in left-wing politics, her screenwriting career was cut short.*

Platon (b. 1968)   "Service"   154

A staff photographer at The New Yorker, *Platon was raised in Greece by his English mother and Greek father until the age of seven, when his family returned to London. He attended St. Martin's School of Art, and after receiving his BA with honors in Graphic Design, he was then awarded an MA in photography and fine art at the Royal College of Art. Platon moved to New York in 1998 after working for* George, *the magazine founded by the late John F. Kennedy, Jr. Since the early 1990s, Platon has continued to shoot portrait, fashion and documentary work for a range of international publications, including* The New Yorker, Time Magazine, Rolling Stone, The New York Times Magazine, Vanity Fair, Harpers Bazaar, Esquire, GQ, Newsweek, Arena, The Face, i-D, The Sunday Telegraph, The Observer, *and* The Sunday Times. *Platon photographed Russian Premier Vladimir Putin for* Time Magazine's *2007 Person of the Year Cover, for which he was awarded the coveted 1st prize at the 2008 World Press Photo Contest.*

Sybil Smith (b. 1954)   "Bev Brown"   171

Born in a small Vermont town, Sybil Smith graduated from Middlebury College in 1977 and Pace University in 1981. She has worked as a nurse in Mississippi, Alaska, North Carolina and now Vermont. Her work has appeared in many publications, including Yankee, The Sun, Harvard Review, The Crescent Review, *and* New England Review.

John Stone, MD (1936 – 2008)   "An Infected Heart"   176

A cardiologist, John Stone taught at Emory University School of Medicine, where he created one of the medical school's first courses on medicine and literature. In addition to medical textbooks and research articles, Stone wrote poetry and short stories, winning numerous awards. He was inducted into the Georgia Writers Hall of Fame in 2007. Stone co-edited a seminal anthology on literature and medicine, On Doctoring: Stories, Poems and Essays, *which since 1991 has been distributed to all first-year medical school students in the United States.*

Alfred Lord Tennyson (1809 – 1892)   "The Lotos-Eaters"   179
                                                     "Ulysses"   184

Alfred Lord Tennyson was one of the most popular Victorian poets, beginning with his first published collection of poems written when he was 17. He was educated at Trinity College, Cambridge, and later succeeded William Wordsworth as Poet Laureate of the United Kingdom. He was buried in Poet's Corner, Westminster Abbey.

Brian Turner (b. 1967)   "AB Negative (The Surgeon's Poem)"   186

Writer and poet Brian Turner received his MFA from the University of Oregon before serving seven years in the US Army, in both Bosnia-Herzegovina and Iraq. His first book of poems, Here, Bullet *(2005) earned several honors and awards, including the Maine Literary Award in Poetry in 2006.*

Walt Whitman (1819 – 1892)   "Old War-Dreams"   188

Walt Whitman was born on Long Island, New York. In his revolutionary work, Leaves of Grass, *he demonstrates his innovative poetic style and content, producing six distinct editions over the course of his lifetime. Ralph Waldo Emerson once described Whitman's poetry as a mixture of the* Bhagavad Gita *and the* New York Herald.

William Carlos Williams (1883 – 1963)   "The Use of Force"   189
                                                      "The Girl with a Pimply Face"   192

Pediatric physician and writer William Carlos Williams worked in his own private medical practice in Rutherford, New Jersey for 41 years. Williams' writings explore themes of humanity, love and death as well as the American experience. In 1963, he received the Pulitzer Prize in poetry and the American Academy of Arts and Letters Gold Medal for poetry.

MAINE HUMANITIES COUNCIL

It is the Maine Humanities Council's mission to engage the people of Maine in the power and pleasure of ideas, encouraging a deeper understanding of ourselves and others, fostering wisdom in an age of information, and providing context in a time of change. The MHC uses the humanities to provide cultural enrichment for all Mainers and as a tool for social change, bringing people together in conversation that crosses social, economic and cultural barriers.

Since its earliest days, the MHC, a private, nonprofit affiliate of the National Endowment for the Humanities, has been recognized for ambitious and innovative projects that explore important and sometimes controversial topics through the lens of the humanities. From a pivotal documentary about the timber industry, to a bold AIDS conference at the beginning of that epidemic, to current long-term projects fueled by issues of social urgency, the MHC's award-winning programs are based on the idea that everyone, regardless of background, can enjoy the transformative power of the humanities. Founded in 1976, the MHC has reached the 21st century with programs that use literature to foster critical thinking and cross-cultural understanding, including reading and discussion groups and seminars for child care providers, low-literacy adults, health care professionals, adults and youth in correctional facilities, and the general public. The MHC also offers a variety of humanities programs for teachers, and provides small grants for humanities projects across Maine.